Margaret and Christine Wertheim

Value and Transformation of Corals

Edited by Udo Kittelmann
for the Frieder Burda Foundation

and by Christine Wertheim
and Margaret Wertheim

MUSEUM FRIEDER BURDA
BADEN-BADEN

WIENAND

Udo Kittelmann

Value and Transformation of Corals

> Now cannot continue to be the age of two-armed,
> radiant-visioned, exterminationist, plastic-saturated,
> fossil-burning, fossil-making prickmen.
>
> Donna Haraway, 2021

Corals are reinventors of life, an inexplicable phenomenon filled with magnificent colors and enigmatic shapes adorning the ocean floor. With a past that goes back millions of years, these sea marvels were not recognized as animals until the eighteenth century. Prior to this scientific discovery, coral held a fascination that can be traced to Ovid's *Metamorphoses*, in which he describes Medusa's blood, after being slain by Perseus, spilling onto the seaweed, transforming it into blood-red coral. This fascination continued not only in depictions of mythological scenes, still lifes, and allegories such as Giorgio Vasari's *Perseus and Andromeda* (1570–72) and Nicolas Poussin's *Perseus and Andromeda: The Origin of Coral* (ca. 1627), but also in the belief of society at large in coral as a protector from disease and evil. Coral's mysterious beauty and biodiversity is full of boundless mutability, constituting an entire ecosystem, and is therefore an important metaphor for our existence. Today, as a result of dramatic climate change around the world these artful creators are losing their beauty and are bleaching, calling on humanity to act quickly and take action in a race against time.

These warnings are nothing new; in the 1970s coral landscapes were already dying, ruined by pollution and overfishing. French filmmaker and pioneer of marine exploration Jacques-Yves Cousteau has captivated viewers with his spectacular films of the underwater world since the 1940s. Cousteau spoke about the fascinating and active coral landscapes that on his later expeditions he found in danger. In our present time, when the effects of technological progress and globalization are unavoidable and frightening headlines about man-made disasters are daily events, people from various disciplines are coming together with a strong commitment to protect the environment: scientists, conservationists, activists, architects, designers, and material engineers among them. New ideas and collective approaches are becoming catalysts for doing something about climate change and taking action now, before it is too late.

In the case of Australian-born, Los Angeles–based artists Margaret and Christine Wertheim, taking action means drawing attention to the ecological systems of the ocean with their collaborative artwork, the *Crochet Coral Reef*. The project has been realized in fifty cities and countries and has roots in mathematics, marine biology, crocheting, feminist art, and environmental studies. This multifaceted endeavor has grown out of the sisters' Institute For Figuring, a nonprofit organization they founded in Los Angeles to engage audiences with the "aesthetic and poetic dimensions of science and mathematics" by playing with materially embodied forms and techniques. In the *Crochet Coral Reef* project, traditional yarn-based craft practices are used to fabricate complex mathematical structures and to assemble these into large-scale Gesamtkunstwerks in which hundreds or thousands of people participate. In her 2009 TED Talk, Margaret explains that the curly shapes seen on corals, seaweed, sponges, and nudibranchs result from a kind of geometry known as "hyperbolic," an alternative to the Euclidean variety we usually learn. Cnidarians have been making such forms for millions of years, and for humans the best way to emulate them is with crochet.

The exhibition *Value and Transformation of Corals* at the Museum Frieder Burda in Baden-Baden presents a unique collection of the Wertheims' crocheted coral reefs, including a *Bleached Reef*, a *Toxic Reef* crafted from plastic, a giant grove of *Coral Forests*, and a collection of miniature *Pod Worlds* composed from finely wrought pieces in crochet and beading. Also on display will be several new works, including two *Nudibranch Reefs* evoking the famous hyperbolic animals. Adding another novel dimension to the project is a large-scale sampler composed of tatted letters paying homage to the project's most committed contributors, for following in the tradition of feminist art practitioners, the Wertheims work collaboratively with locals, aiming to draw forth the creative potentials residing in all people—especially women steeped in craft skills.

The collaborative aspect of the project is also manifest in the creation of *Satellite Reefs*, site-specific community works where people from a given region crochet and assemble their own reefs, and exhibit these alongside the Wertheims' installations. At the Museum Frieder Burda, the *Baden-Baden Satellite Reef* is the latest of these people-powered simulations. We are delighted that so many participants took part in the open call "Crochet for the Oceans" that the museum announced on its website in spring 2021. Comprising more than forty thousand individual crochet coral pieces—by far the most of any *Satellite Reef* endeavor—crafted by over four thousand contributors across Germany and neighboring countries, the woolly archipelago of Baden-Baden subreefs is truly the Great Barrier Reef of crochet coral seascapes.

In November Christine traveled to the museum to work with a team of local women to curate all the coral pieces on six large-scale islands—each one a

→ View of the foyer with the wall panel
*Baden-Baden Satellite Reef: Five Fathoms
Deep* and the LED panel on the façade

purpose-built, three-dimensional topography designed by Christine and built by the Museum Frieder Burda's superb construction team, thereby transforming thousands of individuals pieces into an aesthetic whole, a vibrant entangling of art, craft, mathematics, and community labor. Working together in a tactile way and simultaneously raising awareness of the impact of global warming on coral reefs and ocean degradation, this installation plays a vital role in the overall exhibition.

The Wertheims' dedication to coral reefs derives in part from their childhood in Queensland, the home state of the Great Barrier Reef, itself the largest living structure in the world—visible even from outer space—that is now threatened with extinction. Just as living corals are communal organisms collaboratively building vast aquatic paradises, the Wertheims create a space for communities to generate art together, offering a tender retort to the concept of the singular artistic "genius." With the *Crochet Coral Reef* project, people from all walks of life are invited to play with scientific and mathematical ideas through needlework techniques that emulate the ways living corals generate themselves. Here the power of female craft is joined with the long history of technical and scientific representation. At once intimate and monumental, privately performed and publicly displayed, the *Crochet Coral Reef* serves to highlight our intuitive understanding about environmental protection, sustainability, global warming, and the role we must all play as individuals, and as a social whole, for protecting the precarious riches of nature.

I truly hope that this exhibition will create a dialogue between natural sciences and art in a new context, bringing more attention to the natural and cultural history of these endangered creatures and, with this in mind, hopefully protecting them.

After the long preparation time of this exhibition, I would personally like to thank Margaret and Christine Wertheim for their commitment, trust, and artistic vision. I owe my sincere thanks to the entire team at the museum, especially Judith Irrgang and Christiane Righetti, for their outstanding input and dedication. I am grateful to Kathrin Dorfner for her guidance in overseeing the team involved in the spectacular construction of the *Baden-Baden Satellite Reef*, and to Martina Schulz, Christina Humpert, Charlotte Reiter, Susan Reiss, and Silke Habich as well as the entire team of the art workshop and twenty seamstresses for being part of this project that underlines the philosophy of the collaborative process, crossing borders and languages. A big thank-you is due to Arnd Merkle and his technical team for constructing the reef mounds. I would also like to express my gratitude to our sponsor, EnBW Energie Baden-Württemberg AG. Finally, I would like to thank Henning Schaper, the director of the Museum Frieder Burda, for his continuous support and partnership in the preparation for this exhibition, and I would especially like to extend my sincere gratitude to Elke Burda for her enthusiasm and passion in addressing important global topics.

Baden-Baden Satellite Reef: Five Fathoms Deep

Detail of *Baden-Baden Satellite Reef—Toxic*, with the wall text listing the names of the four thousand contributors in the background

Spire corals with capacitor crabs by
Christine and Margaret Wertheim, 2021

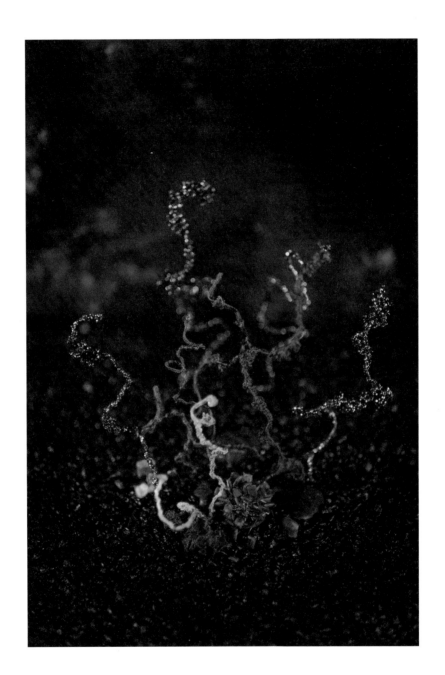

Donna Haraway

Sym-chthonic Tentacular Worldings: An SF Story for the *Crochet Coral Reef*

The *Crochet Coral Reef* is an SF story of string figures, science fact, science fiction, stitched fantasies, and speculative fabulation. This hyperbolic reef is material, figurative, collaborative, tentacular, worldly, dispersed within the tissues and across the surfaces of terra, playful, serious, mathematical, artistic, scientific, fabulous, feminist, exceeding gender, and multispeciesist. Its story is brave; the *Crochet Coral Reef* risks making—actually making—real and fabulated things together in order to open up still-possible times for flourishing on a diverse earth. The time for this story is now; and without overturning the old prick stories, the time could be too short. The threads of the stitched figures made by the tentacular ones could be cut; or, just possibly, the human and more-than-human beings of the planet could loop and knot and tie and braid in generative play tanks and open matrices for still-possible ongoingness.

The *Crochet Coral Reef* takes shape in terran holobiomes inhabited by myriad tentacular ones in a time of response-ability that we yearn to name the Chthulucene. The reef holobiome is the whole assemblage of diverse species, whose living and dying well in ongoing generations and lateral weavings depend on the health of the symbiotic animal cnidarians and algae-like zooxanthellae of the coral. Now cannot continue to be the age of two-armed, radiant-visioned, exterminationist, plastic-saturated, fossil-burning, fossil-making prickmen. Now is already the surging, hyperbolic, non-Euclidean time of many- and snaky-armed ones entangled in the collaborative work and play of caring for and with other earthlings amidst hot and acid seas laced with every kind of toxin. This is the time for overthrowing both the overreaching Anthropocene and the petrodollar-ensorcelled Capitalocene in order to nurture still possible flourishing, still possible recuperation, still possible arts for living in multispecies sympoiesis on a damaged planet. This is the time of consequences.

The Chthulucene draws its name from the awe-ful chthonic ones, the abyssal entities of the underworld, those ongoing generative and destructive powers beneath seas and airs and lands, those who erupt into the affairs of the well-ordered, upward-gazing, progress-stunned, and star-besotted ones, who forget and so dismember their multispecies-tangled flesh. The Gorgons, especially mortal and snaky-headed Medusa, whose blood from her severed head gave rise to the corals of the western sea, are tentacular chthonic powers. They are not finished. The gorgeous sea whips and sea fans of the reefs—the Gorgonia of modern biology—remind terrans of their collaborative mortal lives that are at risk to each other. The chthonic ones empower the symbiotic coral reefs and all the other holobiomes of a thriving earth. These are the powers that the makers of the *Crochet Coral Reef* stitch in non-Euclidean yearning and solidarity.

Sym- means "with"; *poiesis* means "making"; sympoiesis, "making-with." Nothing makes itself, nothing assembles itself, living and dying well as mortal terrans must be sym-chthonic, or they are not at all. The *Crochet Coral Reef* is sym-chthonic. It is for and with the multispecies critters, including human people, of the deep and ongoing earth. The *Crochet Coral Reef* is palpable, polymorphous, terrifying, and inspiring stitchery done with every sort of fiber and strand, looped by tens of thousands of people in dozens of nations, who come together to stitch care, beauty, and response-ability in play tanks. This SF worlding is enabled by Margaret and Christine Wertheim's outrageous, chthonic symbiosis of science, mathematics, art, activism, women's fiber arts, environmentalism, fabulation, and sheer love of the critters of terra. This is truly an Institute For Figuring.

Kayleigh C. Perkov

Between Knowledge and Comfort: The *Crochet Coral Reef* and Data Physicalization

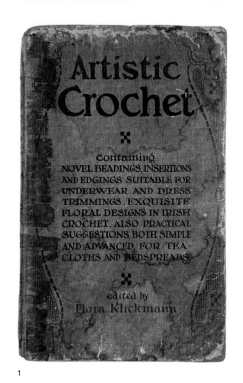

1

Fiber holds information. In the structure of twists, knots, or braids, in the material traces of vegetal and animal threads, fiber not only tells of the process behind its production but can also be used to store and communicate information. The systematic use of fiber for storing data has proven to be transcultural and transhistorical. In the Incan Empire of South America (ca. 1400–1532 A D) knotted cords called *khipu* ↗ fig. 4 served as accounting devices capable of tallying large datasets and potentially functioned as a symbolic language capable of recording life narratives.[1] Hundreds of years later, a cascade of convergent inventions in France led to the punch-card controls of the Jacquard loom, which fine-tuned the processes of automation and information storage in textile creation. This loom, famously, helped inspire the British nineteenth-century mathematician and inventor Charles Babbage to envision the first computer, which he called the "Analytical Engine."[2] A broad array of literature has pointed out these—and many more—connections between the uses of fiber and the information-oriented thinking that has come to dominate our current moment.[3]

For many, finding the characteristics of algorithmic thinking—pattern recognition, communication, control—within fiber is a moment of epiphany ↗ fig. 3. It is a radical act, one that reclaims technological knowledge from a narrative often cast as male and Western, and instead situates it within a broader field of human practice. In its insistence on grappling with information through fiber, the *Crochet Coral Reef* both references this long history of knowledge production, as well as gestures toward current trends of individuals trying to gain knowledge through fiber practices.

Fiber not only holds information but also produces new knowledge. Two inspirations behind the *Crochet Coral Reef* demonstrate the ways in which working with fiber can build new ways of knowing. As Margaret Wertheim describes elsewhere in this volume, the *Reef* took its initial impetus from mathematician Daina Taimina's "hyperbolic crochet." In mathematics, hyperbolic planes are notoriously difficult to model materially and attempts made of paper have proven flimsy and fragile. Taimina's method of creating hyperbolic forms using a simple crocheting pattern highlighted the intricacy of the structure and became a powerful pedagogical tool in college classrooms. Building on Taimina's discovery, Margaret and Christine Wertheim modified the underlying algorithm, adding in the elements of chance and contingency to create a dizzying variety of riotously frilly forms. The uncanny similarity of these hyperbolic shapes to living corals and other marine organisms, such as sponges and kelps, inspired them to develop the dynamic ecology of a crochet coral reef. In addition, the Wertheim sisters were driven by an "awareness that the Great Barrier Reef was being devastated" by human actions, a consciousness all the more salient as they had grown up in the state of Queensland, Australia. A gallows joke they shared together on the night they began was that if the Great Barrier Reef were ever to disappear, their crochet one

1   For a discussion of the language capabilities of *khipu*, see Sabine Hyland, "Writing with Twisted Cords: The Inscriptive Capacity of Andean Khipus," *Current Anthropology* 58, no. 3 (2017): 412–19.

2   Paul Ceruzi, *Computing: A Concise History* (Cambridge, MA: MIT Press, 2012), 5.

3   There is a particularly rich vein of scholarship in regard to Babbage's collaborator, Ada Lovelace; for a classic example of this scholarship, see Sadie Plant, *Zeros and Ones: Digital Women and the New Technoculture* (London: Fourth Estate, 1997). Other scholars have worked to point out the centrality of the labor of women of color in the history of computing; see Lisa Nakamura, "Indigenous Circuits: Navajo Women and the Racialization of Early Electronic Manufacture," *American Quarterly* 66, no. 4 (2014): 919–41. For an example of how references to the feminized labor of textiles have been used by the computer industry, see Kayleigh Perkov, *The Computer Pays Its Debt: Women, Textiles, And Technology, 1965–1985* (Asheville: The Center for Craft, 2020).

Fig. 2 → Justin Connelly, left: three tempestries for Utqiagvik, Alaska, representing (left to right) 1925, 2010, and 2016; right: two tempestries for Death Valley, California, representing (left to right) 1950 and 2016. 2018 at FutureFest in Anacortes, Washington

2

could serve as a facsimile.[4] In this way, the *Crochet Coral Reef* acts as a structure through which people can learn about the world through the act of making: both the structure that underlies hyperbolic geometry, and, metaphorically, the structure of threat that human activity poses to the natural world.

Textiles are never defined solely by the information they hold; their final forms are a summation of process, pattern, and materials. Likewise, how we understand information is always impacted by how it is presented. From today's vantage the *Crochet Coral Reef* can be seen as a strong percussor to the emerging concept of data physicalization. This practice extends upon "data visualization"—the charts and graphics seen in countless newspapers and workplace presentations—to include projects that extend into three-dimensions, often playing upon the sense of touch but sometimes also including a sonic or even taste-based element.[5] Data physicalizations operate under two assumptions: firstly, physical forms help abstract data to feel more real, more visceral, more present; and secondly, that this feeling of reality entreats people to act on social issues. Those working in computer science, data science, and design have heralded physicalizations as a way to create a deeper and more profound relationship with data.[6] As Margaret Wertheim points out, each piece within the entirety of the *Crochet Coral Reef* is itself a data

4   Lawrence Weschler, "The Hyperbolic Crochet Coral Reef," *Virginia Quarterly Review* 87, no. 3 (Summer 2011), https://www.vqronline.org/vqr-gallery /hyperbolic-crochet-coral-reef (accessed October 8, 2021).

5   The Data Physicalization wiki has an ever-growing list of data physicalization projects; see http://dataphys.org /list/ (accessed October 8, 2021).

6   Yvonne Jansen et al., "Opportunities and Challenges for Data Physicalization," in *Proceedings of the 33rd Annual ACM Conference on Human Factors in Computing Systems* (New York: ACM, 2015), 3230.

point in the vast set of all possible hyperbolic and non-Euclidean forms.[7] Though every entry in the *Crochet Coral Reef* is inspired by the same starting pattern, the diversity within the project is endless.

Such differences result partly from each maker's choice in regard to modifying the pattern (the crochet "code"), and partly from differences between the weights and types of threads, the tension employed during crochet, and other physical properties of the yarn and the makers ↗ figs. 5, 6. As Christine Wertheim explores in one of her essays in this volume, the *pattern* employed in the creation of textiles is never the final story ↗ fig. 1; the qualities of the materials also determine how the pieces will unfold in the real world, and likewise the makers leave their marks through the gestural idiosyncrasies of each person's crochet technique. In projects that purposely manifest data, this relational aspect is essential and can produce not only new knowledge, but also create new responses. As information design theorist Dietmar Offenhuber has phrased it "[d]ata physicalization brings data from the unambiguous symbolic space into the real world, where data is a more complicated affair. As the physical manifestation of a data set becomes more elaborate and sensorily rich, data and display cannot be neatly separated."[8] Rather than seeing data as abstracted away from lives and bodies, we see them in relation to their makers, and as viewers, we can see them in relation to ourselves.

Fiber allows people to process information; it channels anxiety, giving worried hands a task to think with. The *Crochet Coral Reef* began in 2005, around the time that scientists were beginning to appreciate the immensity of human impacts on the climate. No longer the problem of an ill-defined future, images of melting icebergs, and reports on the bleaching of the Great Barrier Reef brought the problem into the present.[9] In the decade and a half since, these impacts have become ever more omnipresent—living reefs are now in danger of disappearing entirely marine biologists warn us.[10] Handicrafts give anxious bodies a task to worry through, a way to channel anxiety. By 2016 multiple projects had turned to fiber to physicalize the globe's rising temperature. One example is the Tempestry Project ↗ fig. 2, which began in response to the Trump administration's obstinate denial of climate change.[11] Project founders urged knitters to physicalize weather data using bands of colors, with each row charting local daily temperatures ↗ fig. 2. Circulating on social media, makers talked about the ways in which physicalizing this data forced them to stop, look, and acknowledge patterns within their own immediate environment. Some talked about the ways in which they might have experienced a shrinking ice-skating season but were unable to conceptualize it as part of a broader trend until the temperatures coalesced into a pattern through fibers and needles.

These responses can even occur among experts in the data; perhaps most powerfully among them. Marine scientist Joan Sheldon, for example, created a scarf

7   Interview with the author, June 2021.

8   Dietmar Offenhuber, "What We Talk about When We Talk about Data Physicality," *IEEE Computer Graphics and Applications* 40, no. 6 (2020): 25–37.

9   For an overview of the role images played in raising an awareness of climate change, see Finis Dunaway, *Seeing Green: The Use and Abuse of American Environmental Images* (Chicago: University of Chicago Press, 2015), 258–76.

10 Scott Fraser Heron et al., "Impacts of Climate Change on World Heritage Coral Reefs: A First Global Scientific Assessment." (Paris: UNESCO, 2017).

11 Katharine Schwab, "Crafting Takes a Dark Turn in the Age of Climate Crisis," *Fast Company*, January 1, 2019, https://www.fastcompany.com /90290800/crafting-take-a-dark-turn -in-the-age-of-climate-crisis?position =14&campaign_date=02262019 (accessed October 8, 2021).

33rd Row.—2 bl, 3 sp, 2 bl, 1 sp, 1 bl, 13 sp, 4 bl, 16 sp, 2 bl.

34th Row.—2 bl, 35 sp, 2 bl, 3 sp, 2 bl.

35th Row.—2 bl, 3 sp, 2 bl, 8 sp, 5 bl, 20 sp, 2 bl.

36th Row.—2 bl, 19 sp, 7 bl, 7 sp, 3 bl, 2 sp, 2 bl.

37th Row.—2 bl, 2 sp, 2 bl, 6 sp, 9 bl, 19 sp, 2 bl.

38th Row.—2 bl, 20 sp, 4 bl, 1 sp, 4 bl, 5 sp, 2 bl, 2 sp, 2 bl.

39th Row.—2 bl, 2 sp, 2 bl, 3 sp, 4 bl, 2 sp, 4 bl, 19 sp, 2 bl.

40th Row.—2 bl, 20 sp, 5 bl, 1 sp, 3 bl, 3 sp, 2 bl, 2 sp, 2 bl.

41st Row.—2 bl, 2 sp, 2 bl, 2 sp, 3 bl, 1 sp, 4 bl, 6 sp, 4 bl, 10 sp, 2 bl.

42nd Row.—2 bl, 9 sp, 6 bl, 7 sp, 10 bl, 2 sp, 2 bl.

43rd Row.—2 bl, 2 sp, 4 bl, 1 sp, 2 bl, 3 sp, 3 bl, 3 sp, 9 bl, 8 sp, 2 bl, 10 ch to turn.

44th Row.—2 bl, 10 sp, 12 bl, 4 sp, 3 bl, 1 sp, 5 bl, 2 sp, 2 bl, 5 ch to turn.

45th Row.—For 1 sp, 3 more sp, 2 bl, 2 sp, 2 bl, 2 sp, 3 bl, 5 sp, 4 bl, 2 sp, 2 bl, 10 sp, 2 bl.

46th Row.—10 ch for 2 bl, 12 sp, 2 bl, 2 sp, 4 bl, 3 sp, 4 bl, 1 sp, 3 bl, 3 sp, 2 bl, turn with 5 ch.

47th Row.—2 sp, 1 bl, 3 sp, 8 bl, 3 sp, 6 bl, 13 sp, 2 bl.

48th Row.—2 bl, 14 sp, 4 bl, 4 sp, 6 bl, 4 sp, 2 bl, 2 sp.

49th Row.—6 bl, 4 sp, 3 bl, 23 sp, 2 bl, 10 ch to turn.

50th Row.—2 bl, 19 sp, 4 bl, 9 sp, 1 bl, 2 sp, 2 bl, 1 sp.

51st Row.—2 sp, 1 bl, 2 sp, 3 bl, 6 sp, 6 bl, 18 sp, 2 bl.

52nd Row.—2 bl, 17 sp, 8 bl, 3 sp, 3 bl, 1 sp, 4 bl.

53rd Row.—2 sp, 1 bl, 1 sp, 1 bl, 3 sp, 11 bl, 17 sp, 2 bl.

54th Row.—2 bl, 17 sp, 2 bl, 2 sp, 4 bl, 4 sp, 2 bl, 1 sp, 2 bl, 2 sp.

55th Row.—3 sp, 1 bl, 2 sp, 2 bl, 3 sp, 4 bl, 2 sp, 2 bl, 17 sp, 2 bl, 10 ch to turn.

56th Row.—2 bl, 20 sp, 6 bl, 3 sp, 2 bl, 3 sp, 1 bl, 3 sp.

57th Row.—1 bl, 3 sp, 1 bl, 3 sp, 2 bl, 3 sp, 4 bl, 21 sp, 2 bl.

58th Row.—2 bl, 12 sp, 4 bl, 11 sp, 2 bl, 4 sp, 1 bl, 3 sp, 1 bl.

59th Row.—1 bl, 3 sp, 1 bl, 5 sp, 2 bl, 9 sp, 6 bl, 11 sp, 2 bl.

60th Row.—2 bl, 10 sp, 2 bl, 2 sp, 4 bl, 7 sp, 2 bl, 4 sp, 4 bl, 3 sp.

61st Row.—2 sp, 6 bl, 3 sp, 6 bl, 3 sp, 4 bl, 2 sp, 2 bl, 10 sp, 2 bl.

62nd Row.—2 bl, 10 sp, 11 bl, 2 sp, 4 bl, 2 sp, 8 bl, 1 sp.

63rd Row.—1 sp, 8 bl, 2 sp, 1 bl, 1 sp, 4 bl, 3 sp, 8 bl, 10 sp, 2 bl.

64th Row.—2 bl, 11 sp, 6 bl, 2 sp, 5 bl, 2 sp, 1 bl, 2 sp, 2 bl, 2 sp, 4 bl, 1 sp.

65th Row.—1 sp, 4 bl, 2 sp, 2 bl, 2 sp, 1 bl, 2 sp, 7 bl, 1 sp, 4 bl, 12 sp, 2 bl.

66th Row.—2 bl, 16 sp, 2 bl, 1 sp, 5 bl, 3 sp, 1 bl, 2 sp, 6 bl, 2 sp.

67th Row.—3 sp, 4 bl, 3 sp, 1 bl, 4 sp, 1 bl, 1 sp, 3 bl, 1 sp, 3 bl, 14 sp, 2 bl.

68th Row.—2 bl, 15 sp, 1 bl, 1 sp, 4 bl, 1 sp, 1 bl, 4 sp, 1 bl, 10 sp.

69th Row.—9 sp, 4 bl, 2 sp, 1 bl, 1 sp, 2 bl, 1 sp, 1 bl, 4 sp, 4 bl, 7 sp, 2 bl.

70th Row.—2 bl, 6 sp, 6 bl, 2 sp, 4 bl, 1 sp, 1 bl, 2 sp, 6 bl, 8 sp.

71st Row.—7 sp, 8 bl, 1 sp, 2 bl, 1 sp, 1 bl, 1 sp, 10 bl, 5 sp, 2 bl.

72nd Row.—2 bl, 5 sp, 2 bl, 2 sp, 5 bl, 1 sp, 2 bl, 1 sp, 1 bl, 2 sp, 8 bl, 7 sp.

73rd Row.—7 sp, 2 bl, 2 sp, 4 bl, 2 sp, 2 bl, 1 sp, 2 bl, 1 sp, 4 bl, 2 sp, 2 bl, 3 sp, 2 bl.

74th Row.—2 bl, 3 sp, 8 bl, 1 sp, 1 bl, 1 sp, 2 bl, 3 sp, 4 bl, 2 sp, 2 bl, 7 sp.

75th Row.—8 sp, 6 bl, 4 sp, 5 bl, 1 sp, 6 bl, 4 sp, 2 bl.

76th Row.—2 bl, 5 sp, 4 bl, 1 sp, 5 bl, 6 sp, 4 bl, 9 sp.

77th Row.—19 sp, 5 bl, 8 sp, 2 bl.

78th Row.—2 bl, 8 sp, 3 bl, 3 sp.

79th Row.—4 sp, 3 bl, 5 sp, 2 bl.

80th Row.—2 bl, 5 sp, 2 bl, 5 sp.

81st Row.—10 sp, 2 bl.

82nd Row.—2 bl, 8 sp.

83rd Row.—4 sp, 4 bl.

84th Row.—4 bl, 4 sp.

85th Row.—4 bl.

86th Row.—4 bl, make 10 ch to increase and turn the work for the second side of corner.

87th Row.—2 bl, 9 sp.

88th Row.—9 sp, 2 bl.

89th Row.—2 bl, 9 sp.

90th Row.—9 sp, 2 bl.

91st Row.—2 bl, 9 sp.

92nd Row.—9 sp, 2 bl.

93rd Row.—2 bl, 9 sp.

94th Row.—9 sp, 2 bl.

95th Row.—2 bl, 9 sp.

96th Row.—9 sp, 2 bl.

97th Row.—2 bl, 9 sp.

98th Row.—9 sp, 2 bl.

99th Row.—2 bl, 9 sp.

100th Row.—7 sp, 2 bl.

101st Row.—2 bl, 7 sp.

102nd Row.—7 sp, 2 bl.

103rd Row.—2 bl, 7 sp.

104th Row.—7 sp, 2 bl.

105th Row.—2 bl, 7 sp.

106th Row.—5 sp, 2 bl.

107th Row.—2 bl, 14 sp, 4 bl, 4 sp, 6 bl, 4 sp.

108th Row.—2 sp, 8 bl, 3 sp, 6 bl, 13 sp, 2 bl.

109th Row.—2 bl, 12 sp, 2 bl, 2 sp, 4 bl, 3 sp, 4 bl, 1 sp, 3 bl, 3 sp, 2 bl, 1 sp.

110th Row.—1 sp, 2 bl, 2 sp, 2 bl.

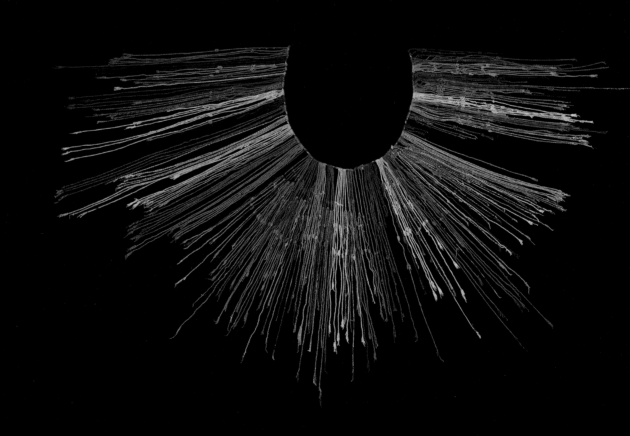

Fig. 3 → Algorithmic crochet patterns resemble computer programs; both use formal codes to describe a precise series of steps. The pages shown here are from the book *Artistic Crochet*, from 1947, which predates most computer languages.

Fig. 4 → Incan *khipu* (recording device based on knots), 1300–1532 AD, Ayacucho, Peru Museo Larco, Lima. ML600004

that physicalized changing historical weather patterns and wore it to a scientific conference. Upon learning what it was, her fellow scientists reached out to touch the piece in order to find their birth year. As Sheldon commented, "[t]hey never would [do this] with a science graph . . . it approaches you in a different way."[12] Others have discussed how making siphons their energy, giving space for thoughtful contemplation. Lea Redmond, creator of the influential "Knit the Sky" project that links data and fiber, describes knitting as "like running with your fingers."[13] The *Crochet Coral Reef* offers a prior example of data physicalization that wrestles with the emotional toll of global warming. More than twenty thousand individuals have crocheted corals for the project so far, a number that testifies to a rising globalized need to materially and psychically engage with the reality of climate change. Some make corals with white thread to physicalize the phenomenon of coral bleaching; other reefs are made with plastic detritus, summoning the phenomenon of oceanic plastic trash. We see these pieces and we hear echoes of news stories and documentaries. We can see the time that each maker spent with these phenomena on their minds, a physicalization of our collective anxiety.

Set within a culture that often devalues feminized labor, fiber's informational richness is frequently occluded by its connotations of warmth. Media responses over data physicalization projects often emphasize their "cozy" nature or their function of helping to "cope." In contrast, Margaret and Christine Wertheim insist on rooting their project within a longer genealogy of feminist practice ↗ fig. 7. They have created a project that spans decades and continents, and which forces us to linger on the fraught and often gendered discourses that ground current data physicalizations. Under the duress of gendered tropes, the softness of fiber can be read as a weakness, an acquiescence to a narrative that says the Earth is too damaged to heal and our best option is nihilistic comfort. Yet set within its entirety, the *Crochet Coral Reef* casts fiber as an active force, one that emphasizes the process of grappling with forms of information so vast they seem to defy human comprehension. The proposition underlying the project is not an easy one, neither denying the facts of climate change, nor slipping into a nihilistic acquiescence, nor romanticizing techno-optimism, there is only a collective of individuals each trying to grapple with immense scales of change. What lies between knowledge and comfort in the face of a changing planet?

12 Schwab, "Crafting Takes a Dark Turn."

13 Schwab.

Figs. 5, 6, page 26 → Thérèse de Dillmont, *La dentelle ténériffe*, Bibliothèque DMC, Mulhouse (Alsace), Dollfus-Mieg & Cie, Mulhouse, Belfort, Paris, ca. 1930, plates 1 and 2

Fig. 7, page 27 → *Ruffled Doilies*, *Clark's J. & P. Coats Crochet Pattern Book* no. 253, Spool Cotton Company, 1949, cover →

LA DENTELLE TÉNÉRIFFE

Dentelles à exécuter avec les articles de Coton, Lin et Soie, marque **D·M·C**

DOLLFUS-MIEG & Cie, Société anonyme
MULHOUSE-BELFORT-PARIS

5

LA DENTELLE TÉNÉRIFFE

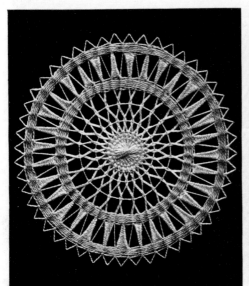 

Dentelles à exécuter avec les articles de Coton, Lin et Soie, marque **D·M·C**

DOLLFUS-MIEG & Cie, Société anonyme
MULHOUSE-BELFORT-PARIS

Ruffled Doilies

D-134 . . . Page 15

Heather Davis

Feeling Crochet, Feeling Coral

1

Fig. 1 → Small sampler, hand-tatted letters on hand-embroidered runner, made especially for the exhibition at the Museum Frieder Burda

The world many of us were born into is not the world that exists now. While in some sense this may have always been the case, the current rate and breadth of change is unprecedented. Whereas in 2005 the disappearance of coral reefs appeared as a mere possibility, today it seems inevitable. How do we collectively begin to think and, more importantly, *feel* this situation?

Not living near the sea, most of us largely witness the demise of coral reefs through highly mediated images. In contrast, Margaret and Christine Wertheim have turned to the material and sculptural qualities of crochet to render their works. This iterative, and highly gendered craft, provides a unique format to rethink our relations with the biological world, for the material methods of making crochet reefs literally duplicate the biological processes by which the "real" ones are made and develop. As Sophia Roosth has argued, here biology, and even evolution, is figured as a mode of craft, when "Reef makers not only mimic but also analogically generate through their crafting . . . new crochet forms."[1] Here, the crafters' hands learn the ways the corals literally grow, using feminine craftwork to mimic the gestation of both individual organisms, their coming together in millions to form reefs, and their development over time. By mimicking the methods of reef formation, the *Crochet Coral Reef* project thus attunes both makers—"reefers"— and viewers to the visceral processual vitality of these oceanic environments, as well as to the disasters now befalling them, such as bleachings and other effects of global warming.

In doing this, the project generates care across distance—between reefers, between reefers and corals, and between reefers, corals, and audience. Donna Haraway describes such relations as "intimacy without proximity."[2] For Haraway, these kinds of closeness avoid both the more benign forms of tourism that contribute in hidden ways to ecosystem degradation, as well as the more insidious traps of "doom and toxic tourism," where disasters are turned into spectacles for consumption. For example, multiple companies offer tours of "the zone" around Chernobyl or Detroit's decaying factories. While direct relations with a tragedy can help fuel our commitment to change, Haraway's perspective offers a different way to think through connection by proposing ways to become attuned without turning calamities into sites of consumption. She cites the *Crochet Coral Reef* as an example, for here reefers identify with coral through embodying the processes of their creation, in practices of handicraft, rather than through devouring them visually. In this way, crochet coral reefers extend their sense of the world with what Eva Hayward calls "fingereyes," a term referencing the synesthetic quality of materialized sensation found in marine organisms whose skin and limbs are also their organs of sight.[3] Crochet reef makers also develop synesthetic qualities, as their crafting hands morph into organs of thought, and perhaps even vision. Thus, as a whole, the *Crochet Reef* is a project concerned with the way *biology is figured as process*, a constant movement or dance between individuals, collectives and

1   Sophia Roosth, "Evolutionary Yarns in Seahorse Valley: Living Tissues, Wooly Textiles, Theoretical Biologies," *Differences: A Journal of Feminist Cultural Studies* 23, no. 3 (2012): 9–41, here 11.

2   Donna Haraway, *Staying with the Trouble: Making Kin in the Chthulucene* (Durham: Duke University Press, 2016), 53.

3   Eva Hayward, "Fingeryeyes: Impressions of Cup Corals," *Cultural Anthropology* 25, no. 4 (2010): 578–99, here 580.

environments. Importantly, it does this through *showing and making*, rather than through argumentation or digital imagery. It is a fully embodied practice.

Initially the project arose from a fascination with the fact that crochet can be used to construct models of complex mathematical surfaces called *hyperbolic* planes. Hyperbolic geometry, an alternative to the geometry we learn in school, describes a non-Euclidean space characterized by "negative curvature"—the opposite of a sphere—that we see in the shape of a "saddle." Although mathematicians did not discover this geometry until the early nineteenth century, and even then thought it couldn't be realized in physical space, feminine crafters have long worked with such forms—in the ruffles around doilies, in lace cuffs and collars, as well as the flounces on little girls' dresses, and the gores that enable women's skirts to flare out and swing. Finally, in 1997, the mathematician and crafter Daina Taimina realized we could use such techniques to make formal models of hyperbolic planes. Building on this insight, the Wertheims discovered that if one deviates from perfection in making such models, the resultant forms strikingly resemble the hypercurved forms found in corals, kelps, and other marine organisms. For such creatures, hyperbolic geometry allows for maximum surface area in a minimal volume. To those without fangs and claws, who feed or breathe through their skins, this mathematical form is a key to survival. In other words, the dramatic shapes and beautiful folds of marine creatures exemplify a *solution* to the problem of lunch, and hyperbolic crochet precisely mimics this evolutionary answer. This exact replication of reef-formation processes in the crocheted siblings is also found in the evolution of the *Crochet Reef* project as a whole, for just as seagoing reefs have slowly evolved more complex individuals and more complex combinations of groupings, over time, the crochet forms have also evolved on both individual and collective levels.

The project in total comprises two kinds of reef. The first is composed of sculptures made and curated by the Wertheim sisters, with further crochet pieces contributed by a small group of skilled crafters from around the world. These "core" reefs operate within a more traditional understanding of contemporary art, with the Wertheims carefully making and arranging affective experiences for viewers. The second category in the project are the *Satellite Reefs* which operate more organically, as an analogue to biological reefs where formations are less curated, and structures more haphazard. Many of these endeavors now have hundreds, even thousands of contributors—the project as a whole has attracted more than twenty thousand participants—so the installations are larger, wilder, less "professional-looking." These local instantiations of collective expression are shown in the country or city where most of the contributors reside, and often embody cultural references from that specific region. In Ireland, reefers drew on the tradition of lacey white "Irish crochet"; in the United Arab Emirates, the *Abu Dhabi Satellite Reef* was constructed around traditional Emirati fishing traps that also evoke the peaks

"In this collaborative process, each person becomes part of a wider whole, analogous to an individual coral 'polyp,' engaging with the slow process of building a collective form. And here we find a similar productive confusion about whether to see the whole as one organism or as a collective."

of mosques; while in Scottsdale, Arizona, crafters used a color palette of yellows and ochres reminiscent of their desert environment; in Mexico, a reef was displayed in a *puesto*, the street kiosks where newspapers are typically sold.

Satellite Reefs often begin with a workshop by Margaret or Christine. From there, institutions and crafters are free to develop their own reef idiosyncratically, with the driving force being the community's own desires and aesthetic predilections. Here, both community and individual agency are activated, mirroring the formation of living reefs that also grow in relation to their local conditions. In this collaborative process, each person becomes part of a wider whole, analogous to an individual coral "polyp," engaging with the slow process of building a collective form. And here we find a similar productive confusion about whether to see the whole as one organism or as a collective.

In the ocean, each coral head is composed of hundreds or thousands of polyps. Furthermore, what we call "coral" is actually a consortium of the coral genome and its products subsisting in symbiotic relationship to photosynthetic algae. In other words, corals are a good example of what Scott Gilbert has termed a "holobiont," that is, a "host," and all its symbionts that rely on one another to survive— a mode of living that confounds the distinction between the singular entity and the whole colony.[4] By providing a different understanding of what is meant by "collective" and "individual," these terms cease to be opposites and instead begin to merge into each other. Similarly, while each person who contributes to a crochet reef can identify their individual contribution, these would not be understood as a *reef* if shown in isolation. Collectivity is as central also to the creation of woolen reefs, as it is necessary to the living ones.

So too, the *Crochet Coral Reef* can be seen a physical expression of what Anna Lowenhaupt Tsing terms the "arts of noticing."[5] Tsing argues that certain acts slow down processes of perception and conceptualization, enabling us to pay a finer grade of attention to the world around us. Such strategies, she argues, help towards a recalibration of the speed of change because they do not operate within modernist narratives of progress, but focus attention on what happens at the edges, in the off time. Crochet operates within this sideways time, as it is often incorporated into leisure and other activities, where noticing is an embodied activity. In crochet, hands "notice" by mirroring the productive labor of the coral polyps. Fingers and wrists ache from iterative activity as they embody their own form of

4   Scott Gilbert and Alfred Tauber, "Rethinking Individuality: The Dialectics of the Holobiont," *Biology & Philosophy* 31 (2016): 839–53.

5   Anna Lowenhaupt Tsing, *The Mushroom at the End of the World: On the Possibility of Life in Capitalist Ruins* (Princeton, NJ: Princeton University Press, 2015), 37.

Fig. 2 → Crafters from the *Föhr Satellite Reef* sorting corals into colors at the Museum Kunst der Westküste, Föhr, Germany, 2012

Fig. 3 → Shari Porter and her daughter with brain-coral mound at Track 16 Gallery, Los Angeles, 2009

Fig. 4 → "Team Finland" (Lotta Kjellberg, Elina Ahlstedt, Noura El Harouny, and Tuija Maija Piironen) curating the *Helsinki Satellite Reef* for the Helsinki Biennial, 2021

2

3

4

Fig. 5 → Crochet reef workshop led by Tija Viksna for the *Latvian Satellite Reef*, which was hosted by and exhibited at Gallerie Consentio Riga, Latvia, 2009

Fig. 6 → Crochet workshop for the *Föhr Satellite Reef* at the Museum Kunst der Westküste, Föhr, Germany, 2012

Fig. 7 → Gabriele von Hollen-Heindorf, chief curator of the *Föhr Satellite Reef*, staging corals at the Museum Kunst der Westküste, Föhr, Germany, 2012

5

6

7

"When we put our efforts together, we may no longer focus on our individual contributions, but we may be able to create worlds of immense beauty that celebrate our inherent interconnections with one another and with other species."

intelligence, their own sensing, feeling, and decision-making while the rest of the body they are attached to is conversing, watching TV, or listening to music.

Crochet and evolution also mimic each other when variations are introduced randomly, when "mistakes" are heightened, chosen, or accentuated because of an aesthetic or functional quality, causing new organisms to emerge.[6] Evolution also happens through the inspiration of the collective, when participants working in tandem with other reefers bounce ideas around and learn from each other.[7] For instance, tightly crocheted coils wrapped around wire to produce vertical forms were started by Evelyn Hardin, then quickly spread throughout the project.

6   See the essay "Matter, Form, and Technology: Materiality Counts" on pages 62–69 in this book.

7   Here, I want to highlight the theory of evolution put forward by Lynn Margulis, who claims that the primary driving force for evolution is not random variation, but rather the exchange of different symbiotic organisms, particularly bacteria.

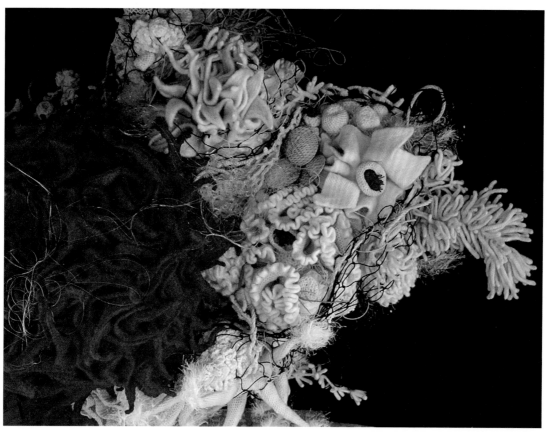

Fig. 9 → Detail of *Bleached Reef*
at the 58th Venice Biennale, 2019

9

Likewise, in 2006, the Wertheims began crocheting "plarn," yarn made from cut-up plastic bags, weaving these synthetic forms into a *Toxic Reef*, as an ongoing commentary on oceanic plastic trash, another byproduct of human activity devasting reefs worldwide. Since then, the plastic side of the project has developed into one of its most important aspects, with many surprisingly anomalous new specimens contributed from reefers worldwide.[8]

The *Crochet Coral Reef* becomes, then, a means to affectively attune ourselves to the dire realities of coral death while refusing to give in to despair. As the Wertheims write: "This is not a project of mourning and loss, but rather, in the face of the terrifying potential for loss, a small figure of hope. We crochet-reefers ourselves are polyps. Our efforts alone can't 'save' coral reefs, but perhaps our installations may encourage viewers to stop for a moment and think about the power of little things."[9] I would go even further, suggesting that the project offers important lessons about the creativity of life itself, the ways that organisms constantly adapt and change, the beauty in the power of becoming. It also offers a profound lesson about political organizing, which is that instead of relying upon individual leaders, we can also build vibrant worlds with a good framework and a dedicated collective. When we put our efforts together, we may no longer focus on our individual contributions, but we may be able to create worlds of immense beauty that celebrate our inherent interconnections with one another and with other species.

[8] For more on this, see the essay "Plasticene Middens and Plastic Fossils, or the Lithospheric Imaginary" on pages 90–97 in this book.

[9] Margaret Wertheim and Christine Wertheim, *Crochet Coral Reef* (Los Angeles: Institute For Figuring Press, 2014), 72.

Pages 36–37: Margaret Wertheim in the *Föhr Satellite Reef*, Museum Kunst der Westküste, Föhr, 2012   →

Margaret and Christine Wertheim

Maintenance Work: Crochet Coral Care Reef

1

What is the *Crochet Coral Reef*? Is it sculpture, installation, museum display, science experiment, handicraft project, or a species of feminist activism? Perhaps it is all these? Above all, we think of it in the tradition of what artist Mierle Laderman Ukeles calls "maintenance work."

In 1969, soon after the birth of her first child, Ukeles found her life divided by the supposedly opposing roles of artist and mother. Frustrated by this imposed division, she sat down one night and in a single session penned a manifesto that would forever change the way some of us think about art. In this revolutionary document, Ukeles proposed that there are two kinds of work: "Development," described as "pure individual creation; the new; change; progress; advance; excitement," and "Maintenance: keep the dust off the pure individual creation; preserve the new; sustain the change; protect progress; defend and prolong the advance; renew the excitement."[1] "Development" encompasses the construction and erection of "original" works, including, in the 1960s and 1970s, such "Conceptual" acts as the writing of manifestos and other purely verbal construction/erections like instructions for making a work, or simply the contract for the sale of a piece that might be nothing more than the contract itself. On the other hand, "maintenance" moves beyond the confines of both traditional and avant-garde artistic milieus to engage with the physical activities of everyday life—especially those concerned with care.

With her manifesto, Ukeles used the avant-garde vehicle of the political declaration to "overturn the avant-garde presumption . . . that freedom in art is grounded in originality—that . . . the 'artist-genius' never repeats (him)self."[2] For Ukeles, this notion was in conflict with the demands and ethics of *motherhood*, which require the constant repetition of mundane tasks. Her manifesto consists of only four widely spaced pages, with page one describing the basic definitions. On the remaining pages she outlines a proposal for an exhibition. The full title of the document is "MANIFESTO FOR MAINTENANCE ART 1969! Proposal for an Exhibition: 'CARE.'" Here, she declares:

> I am an artist. I am a woman. I am a wife. I am a mother. (Random order).
> I do a hell of a lot of washing, cleaning, cooking, renewing, supporting, preserving, etc. Also, (up to now separately) I "do" Art.

Then she introduces her revolutionary proposal, that from now on:

> I will simply do these maintenance everyday things, and flush them up to consciousness, exhibit them, as Art. I will live in the museum . . . and do all these things as public Art activities: I will sweep and wax the floors, dust everything, wash the walls.
> The exhibition area might look "empty" of art, but it will be maintained in full public view.
> MY WORKING WILL BE THE WORK.

1   Mierle Laderman Ukeles, "MANIFESTO FOR MAINTENANCE ART 1969! Proposal for an Exhibition: 'CARE.'" typewritten manifesto, 1969.

2   Sherry Buckberrough, catalog essay for *Mierle Laderman Ukeles/Matrix 137* (Hartford, CT: Wadsworth Atheneum, 1998).

Ukeles spent four years unsuccessfully trying to interest galleries in this proposition. Not until the critic Lucy Lippard asked her to participate in an exhibition of all-female conceptual artists could she get the show mounted—and this in an era when pouring asphalt down a hill or having oneself shot, as did two male contemporaries, was considered high Art. Why were these gestures deemed interesting by the Art world, when Ukeles's actions were not?

More important than cleaning *per se* is the general notion of *service*, or what Ukeles calls "maintenance." As the manifesto makes clear, maintenance includes all labors that support and nurture others, both people and things; whether these be other artworks, as in the cleaning and dusting of a sculpture, or other persons, as in the raising of a child, or caring for a sick partner. Synonyms for Ukeles's "maintenance" might thus be "service" and "care."

In the twenty-first century, a new genre of art called Social Practice aims to blur the boundary between maintenance and development work by incorporating support and care for the *audience* into the art. Here, artists don't just offer a spectacle, they aim to promote the viewer's own creative desires by including these in the production and performance of the work. By this means, an artist can move from the position of unique creator (the artist as genius) to a more faciliatory role, and the audience can shift from being mere spectators to becoming active collaborators. Of course, much depends on the nature of the practice—are the audience merely fabricating the *artist's* work, or are they genuinely contributing something effective of their *own*? Social practice arts include a wide array of activities from making anything with the audience—bread and butter to large-scale collective sculptures and performances—to cooking for or with spectators, or engaging them in intimate conversations, and even sex.

Most major museums now have extensive programs working with artists to create social practice events on their grounds. And artists can have substantial careers in this field. Witness Ukeles, who in the late 1970s became the official artist-in-resident for the New York Department of Sanitation, where one of her first works was to meet, greet and thank all of its thousands of employees for their service to the city in helping to collect and manage its trash.

Yet surviving economically on such work can be hard. Time and again, one hears that the fees paid by institutions for organizing such events don't even cover the cost of materials, let alone the artists' time. For over twenty-five years, Ukeles's residency was official, but unpaid. Such practitioners can only survive economically by working other jobs, such as teaching or design. Supporting oneself directly from social practice is possible only if an artist can turn their work into salable items. After decades of voluntary work, Ukeles began copyrighting her photos and other documents so she could make an income from her oeuvre. But many social

"Among its many guises, the *Crochet Coral Reef* is also a social practice, supporting participants and communities by maintaining an organizational structure within which they can collectively and creatively contribute."

practitioners have no goods to sell. The *events* themselves are their only aesthetic work, and these can't be sold. As such, they are not part of the art world's true economy. A further invisibilizing effect of this differential valuation is that even the documentary evidence of such work will quite likely not be preserved, both because the artists themselves often don't have the resources, and because the institutions don't see the value in it—for them, the event is all that matters. But this writes such practices out of art history, and impedes the artists from advancing financially, or from continuing as artists at all.

Among its many guises, the *Crochet Coral Reef* is also a social practice, supporting participants and communities by maintaining an organizational structure within which they can collectively and creatively contribute. Though invisible to all but the museum staff, with whom we interact, the maintenance of this *organizational structure* is a huge part of the *Reef* project. Emails, websites, tax files, business accounts, storage facilities, crochet instructions, curation, contract negotiation, installation design and execution, book publishing, wall-text production, packing, crating and shipping work, etc.—all these have to be performed over and over again on a weekly, monthly, or yearly basis. Like caring for a child, someone has to actively maintain the organism, or it could not survive, let alone flourish. More than the making of core crochet reefs for exhibition in galleries and museums, the paperwork mountain that maintains the enterprise is the bulk of our contribution to the project. Indeed, this bureaucratic mountain could itself be exhibited as Art, much as Ukeles, and other conceptual artists, have exhibited their paperwork.

But if this kind of work is so highly desired by institutions on one level—the sheer ubiquity of social practice events at contemporary museums suggests this is so— why, on another level, is it so poorly rewarded and valued? For though ubiquitous, most social practice events are commissioned by the outreach arms of museums, rather than by curators inside the gallery proper. Though there are exceptions, it is true to a large degree, and the budgets and status accorded these events indicate their real value within a world where worth is increasingly indexed to sales. The point here is that, while participatory events attract large crowds and generate positive feedback for museums, they don't generate *profit*, for in the end there is nothing to *sell*. And even when there might be something to *keep*, as in leftover objects, or even documentations, often these are not seen as valuable in their own right.[3] One way of looking at this conundrum, in which service-based works are less prized than *things* such as paintings and sculptures, may lie in the economics and theory of what is defined as "work" in its more general sense.

3   For more on this issue, see the piece on the Helsinki Reefs on pages 98–101 in this catalog.

Fig. 2 → Kathleen Greco baking JellyYarn "sand" in her kitchen in Pennsylvania. The pearls, apron, flowered mitts, and pink sandals evoke 1950s "housewife chic."

Kathleen Greco created JellyYarn as a unique vinyl thread for knitting and crochet. She has crafted many pieces for the Crochet Coral Reef with it. When baked slowly at a low temperature, her JellyYarn "sand" becomes soft and pliable, making it ideal for draping over coral mounds.

43

Fig. 3 → Crochet-reefers curating the *Föhr Satellite Reef*, at Museum Kunst der Westküste, Föhr, Germany, 2012

Fig. 4 → Crochet Coral Reef workshop for the *Föhr Satellite Reef*, at Museum Kunst der Westküste, Föhr, Germany, 2012

3

4

Affective, Reproductive, and Immaterial Labor

In modern economic theory dating back to Marx, only labor producing material things counted as value-generating "work"—value here being seen as synonymous with profit. In other words, only *things* were seen as potential commodities. With the rise of the information economy, suddenly, or so it seemed, the idea surfaced that nonmaterial items could also be profitably commodified. Profit-making immaterials include data, software, and other information products. But crucially, they also include "services." Within this shift in economic thinking—induced by the birth of a new kind of men's work—monetizable service-based tasks were initially conceived of as various forms of "consulting"—primarily for the finance, business, and IT sectors.

But, as some political thinkers soon understood—especially women—profit-generating services also include jobs further down the corporate food chain: call-center operatives, flight attendants, waiters, nurses, therapists, and sex workers. "Service" also includes caretakers, such as mothers and homemakers whose labor has traditionally been excluded from official economic reckonings like the GDP. The inclusion of this caretaking labor in the formal economy raises many questions.

In academic terminology, service as profit-generating work is known as *affective labor.* And as Guillermina Altomonte has pointed out, there are many different ways to understand this kind of work.[4] For example, to a political theorist such as Michael Hardt, affective labor is simply one aspect of a more general category called *immaterial labor* that generates nonmaterial goods such as information, knowledge, and service. Hardt argues that "the products" of this labor "are social networks [and] forms of community . . . that is, the power to create society itself."[5] From this perspective, affective labor is "spread throughout the entire workforce," even industrial processes.[6]

By contrast and with regard to Arlie Hochschild's analysis, Altamonte describes the term *affective labor* as the invisible yet intense work embedded in producing and managing our emotions."[7] Here she includes "caring, listening, comforting, reassuring," and even smiling.[8] Affective labor in this sense requires the worker to treat the consumer like a guest, an expectation now embedded in all-customer facing jobs, of which there is an ever-proliferating variety. Hochschild's categorization, with its focus on human interaction and care, does *not* include the informatic intangibles of software and data management. And as Altamonte notes, affective labor in her terms is almost always gendered, "since it has been historically associated with female qualities" and activities.[9] Thus, since the 1970s we have witnessed a seismic shift from an industrial to a service-oriented economy that has induced a general feminization of the labor force.

4   Guillermina Altomonte, "Affective Labor in the Post-Fordist Transformation," Public Seminar, May 8, 2015, https://publicseminar.org/2015/05/affective-labor-in-the-post-fordist-transformation/ (accessed October 6, 2021).

5   Michael Hardt, "Affective Labor," *Boundary* 26, no. 2 (Summer 1999): 89–100.

6   Hardt, "Affective Labor."

7   Hochschild examines the alienation and exploitation of emotional work in the services market. See Arlie Russell Hochschild, "Feeling Management," in *The Managed Heart* (Berkeley and Los Angeles: University of California Press, 1983).

8   Altamonte, "Affective Labor."

9   Altamonte.

Fig. 5 → Crochet Coral Reef workshop for the *Eindhoven Satellite Reef* at Van Abbemuseum, 2018

Figs. 6, 7 → Reefers of the *Baden-Baden Satellite Reef*, Museum Frieder Burda, Baden-Baden, 2022

5

6

7

"The *Crochet Coral Reef* can also be seen as a work of affective labor, for the bulk of its activity consists in maintaining the organizational infrastructure that enables a collective project to develop and thrive. Of particular note here is the labor of negotiating credit for the thousands of participants who contribute to the community-made *Satellite Reefs*."

As Altomonte points out, however, the movement of care work from the home to the marketplace has *not* led to a redefinition of the major care activity of child-rearing, known as "reproductive labor." It has simply resulted in the creation of new "second-rate" jobs that are mostly performed by women, often of socially disadvantaged groups racially and ethnically marked.[10] The shift thus further divides women—who could be a potentially unified gender grouping—into a disunified set of hierarchized, and even oppositional classes.

Adding to the gender-related problems of the new economy is Hardt's idea that affective labor is merely a subcategory of a more general form of immaterial labor. For this obscures the fact that knowledge and information—still generally associated with men—are greatly more prized than the more embodied services of cleaning, caring, and emotional management that are still often associated with and performed by women. In other words, as Altomonte notes, even in the new economy, not all types of affective labor are valued equally. Thus, while the concept of "affective" labor opens the idea that "women's" work can also be value-generating, that is, profitable, it does not erase the distinction or the differential valorization between work coded as feminine and that coded as masculine.

Similar differential valuations occur in the art world, where works using methods and materials like bitumen and guns—usually seen as "masculine"—count more, are generally higher priced, and are more frequently preserved than those employing feminine-coded modes such as crochet or cleaning. It could thus be said that any method or material smacking of feminine-coded service is less likely to be seen as profit-making Art, or even as Art at all, than work employing mediums associated with normative ideas about masculinity. Ukeles was right: the world is still divided into two kinds of work—the Development of Erections, and the Maintaining and Fluffing of these edifices.

The *Crochet Coral Reef* can also be seen as a work of affective labor, for the bulk of its activity consists in maintaining the organizational infrastructure that enables a collective project to develop and thrive. Of particular note here is the labor of negotiating credit for the thousands of participants who contribute to the

10 Altamonte, "Affective Labor." Here, Altomonte refers to considerations uttered by Susanna Uhde.

community-made *Satellite Reefs*. As Ukeles's manifesto points out, the Art world is geared to the display and crediting of work by unique "artist-geniuses." Works made by countless anonymous citizens disrupt this system of valuation by asking that institutions include the names of hundreds or even thousands of people on gallery walls. Moving institutions to a place where they are willing to display the names of so many people, thereby acknowledging them all as co-artists, often requires a great deal of time and persuasion on our part as artists, for it goes against not only the long history of solo-artist attribution, but also pushes against basic museological formats for gallery signage, wall texts, announcement cards, and so on. These traditional apparatuses of crediting are much in need of revision and loosening if museums and galleries want to ethically incorporate community-based work in their repertoires of practice.

How *does* one appropriately acknowledge four thousand collaborators on a single artwork? This is a question, and a challenge, posed by the *Crochet Coral Reef*, one that affords no simple solution, but rather imposes on us as artists, and on our various host institutions, an ongoing duty of care.

Page 48: Detail of *Coral Forest—Medusa* featuring worm-stitch corals by Helle Jorgensen and "bubble corals" by Jane Canby

Page 49: Crocheted octopus by Helen Bernasconi, made of yarn from her own sheep—hand sheared, hand spun, hand dyed

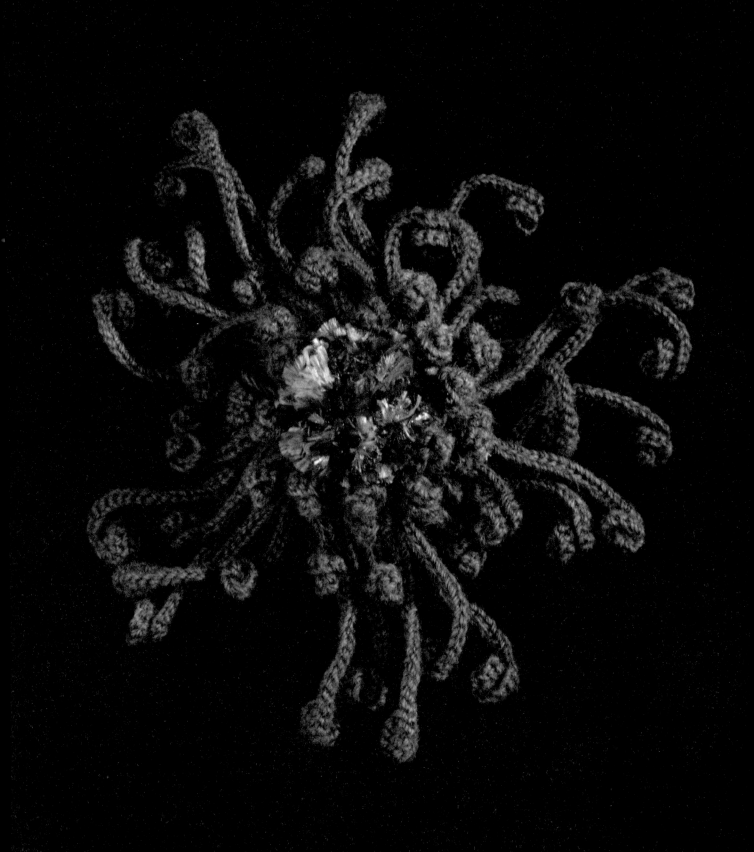

Christine and Margaret Wertheim

Baden-Baden Satellite Reef: A Parallel Universe of Creative Female Energy

1

Fig. 1 → Many helping hands arrange
and sew the corals to create large reefs.

From all over Germany, packages came flooding through the mail: small ones, large ones, finely wrapped parcels elegantly hand-addressed, and lumpy bundles bursting with life even before they were opened. Inside them all were crocheted corals crafted in every conceivable color, and from a vast array of materials including heavy-gauge hand-spun wool, fine mercerized cottons, synthetic yarns, cut-up plastic bags, and many other fibers both shop-bought and home-improvised. Over six months in late 2021, nearly forty thousand of these crafted creatures found their way to the Museum Frieder Burda by hitherto unimagined migratory paths that brought them from the local region of Baden-Baden; from the cities of Berlin, Frankfurt am Main, Hamburg, and Cologne; and from tiny villages at the edge of the North Sea and deep within the Black Forest. Some arrived from Switzerland, the Netherlands, Austria, France, Italy, finally from all over Europe, even from Bulgaria, and also from overseas, the United States, Canada, and Australia!

This crafty outpouring was the raw material from which the *Baden-Baden Satellite Reef* was to be constructed, this now-vast archipelago of wooly coral islands displayed in the upper gallery of the museum, and on a giant "coral wall" that evokes both the long history of sewing and quilting bees traditionally performed by women in their homes, and newer histories of monumental fiber sculpture by professional artists such as Nick Cave, Sheila Hicks, Mike Kelley, Faith Ringgold, and Joana Vasconcelos.

More than four thousand people—most of them women—contributed corals for this latest addition to the growing constellation of *Satellite Reefs* around the world, a globe-enwrapping set of sibling installations that together constitutes one of the largest, most enduring community art happenings ever. During the past sixteen years, fifty such reefs have spawned from the original seed of the *Crochet Coral Reef* we started in our Los Angeles living room in 2005. Emulating the process by which living reefs send out spawn to precipitate the growth of new reefs elsewhere, our *Crochet Reef* spawns novel iterations in museums and galleries made by local crafters who come together in collective acts of making to build their own versions of a reef.

If one can trace a biological metaphor here in the mechanism by which crochet reefs replicate, there is also a more metaphysical story to be told, for the *Crochet Coral Reef* project has opened a kind of portal for channeling creative female energy. When we started our first reef, Christine and I imagined a few dozen crafters might join us in this quixotic entangling of crochet, mathematics, marine biology, and environmental reflection. Yet we seem to have generated a wormhole to a vast universe of female craft potential that has to go *somewhere*. Pouring through the transom has come an exponentiating number of corals, exceeding even our wildest dreams: over two thousand at the Hayward Gallery in London (2009), four thousand at the Smithsonian in Washington (2010), five thousand at the Helsinki

Fig. 2 → The size of the packages arriving
at the museum increased every day.

Figs. 3, 4 → The corals are sorted and composed by color and form. The quantity
and diversity are overwhelming, presenting a challenge to Kathrin Dorfner's team.

Biennial (2020–21), and now forty thousand in Baden-Baden. We yearn to call
the pluripotent zone from which these wonders emerge the *Crochetcene*, and hail
it as a valuable wellspring for future art production. Indeed, other community
craft projects have already been inspired by the methodologies we've developed for
collective Reef making, including the "5000 Poppies" project in Australia, which
ultimately resulted in over one hundred thousand knitted and crocheted poppies
as a tribute to soldiers who died in World War I.

Community art-making requires not just imagination and skill and many nim-
ble hands, but also what we may call "technologies of collaboration." As feminist
science studies scholar Donna Haraway notes at the start of this book, "nothing
makes itself," and to make collaborative works on a vast scale requires a "back-
stage'" managerial infrastructure and framework to support and sustain the aesthetic work being generated for display. In this sense, making a *Satellite Reef* is
akin to putting on a play. Just as a theatrical performance begins with a *script*
that is given local flavor through the specificities of casting, set design, costum-
ing, lighting, and cultural setting, each *Satellite Reef* is a local enactment of a
"script'" that lays out a general plan of action to be implemented in each different
cultural setting through choices about community outreach, display techniques,
reef architecture, color groupings, and so on. Will a local reef extend over low
pedestals, or creep up the walls? Will it be arranged by hues—a red section, a blue
section, and so on—or by mixing pallets, as was done so well in Helsinki? Each

4

"Each reef becomes an opportunity for a local team to become directors of their own production, thereby inviting *citizens* to the curatorial table, a place generally reserved in the art world for a select elite."

reef becomes an opportunity for a local team to become directors of their own production, thereby inviting *citizens* to the curatorial table, a place generally reserved in the art world for a select elite.

For the Baden-Baden installation, Christine traveled early on in the process to work with local "reefers" and museum preparators to help conceive and design the staging as a series of low-slung islands featuring conical protrusions, "coral trees," deep fissures, and poles on which are showcased spectacular corals. But *so many* corals continued to pour in from the Crochetcene zone, and the islands filled faster than they could be built. What to do with the extravagant excess? A plan was conceived to have them fill a wall in the museum using the mass of additional corals as a kind of "paint" to render a gigantic conceptual image of wooly magnitude. This monumental work, made possible by the energies of so many mainly female "reefers," is also a testimony to the unceasing potential residing in the script of the *Crochet Coral Reef* project. What might different communities achieve with this collaborative technology? As in nature, there is no end to the possibilities for creative surprise.

We would especially like to thank the core curatorial team who helped to develop these woolly masterpieces: Kathrin Dorfner, Martina Schulz, Christina Humpert, Charlotte Reiter, Susan Reiss, and Silke Habich as well as the entire team of the museum's art workshop and twenty seamstresses. In addition, our admiration goes out to all the thousands of people who contributed corals and the immensity of their work.

Doug Harvey

Coming Raveled: An Annelidan Taxonomy; The *Crochet Coral Reef* as Outsider Art

1

Any attempt to discuss Christine and Margaret Wertheim of the Institute For Figuring's *Crochet Coral Reef* necessitates the opening of a whole can of worms. There's the Environmentalist worm. There's the Feminist worm. There's a Formalist worm and a Conceptualist worm. There's a big Anti-Hierarchical Rhizomatic worm. There's the Relational Art/Social Sculpture worm. There's the Craft-as-Art worm and the Institutional Critique worm. And there's the Outsider Art worm.

It's this last worm that I want to spend some time examining, but there's a problem: these worms have been commingling in the can for a while now, and you can't really untangle and isolate them in any convincing way. For example, your basic Anti-Hierarchical Rhizomatic worm contains segments that are indistinguishable from your Feminist worm. Some experts believe that the Formalist worm and the Conceptualist worm are actually the same worm seen from opposite angles. Then there are other theories. A diagram from 1986 illustrates this still-controversial hypothesis ↗ fig. 2.

Nevertheless, in order to grapple with the idea of applying the "Outsider" designation to an ever-changing collaborative contemporary craft installation that has been displayed at major cultural institutions around the globe, we'll have to grab a handful and see what wriggles to the surface.

Worm the First: Outsider

To consider the *Crochet Coral Reef* as a work of Outsider Art, we have to untangle the complex relationship between the history of erasure of "women's work" from the (art) historical record, the discovery and promotion of the art of various excluded populations huddled under the "Outsider" tent, and the sometimes incompatible strategies employed to attempt to rectify these occlusions.

2

Fig. 3 → Anna Mary Robertson "Grandma"
Moses, *The Quilting Bee*, 1950, oil on pressed board,
private collection, Kallir Research Institute

3

In spite of the fact that Outsider Art and Feminist Art both began to gain popular
and historical traction during the same period—the early 1970s—the breakdown
of noteworthy Outsider artists along gender lines has mysteriously mirrored that
of the conventional art world. Although there are notable exceptions—visionary
English spiritualist Madge Gill; first draft Art Brutista Aloïse Corbaz (who had
an imaginary romance with Kaiser Wilhelm II); former seamstress, abortion-
ist, and railway saboteur turned Prinzhorn Collection dummy-maker Katharina
Detzel ↗ fig. 1; Chicago DIY gutter-glam icon Lee Godie. There are a handful
of others, but the demographics are pretty much in line with Jean Dubuffet's
statement announcing the formation of the (all-male) Compagnie de l'Art Brut:
"We are seeking works that exhibit the abilities of invention and of creation in a
very direct fashion, without masks or constraints. We believe these abilities exist
(at least at times) in every man."[1]

Although concerted efforts have been made to address this imbalance in recent
years, the auction record speaks for itself. A tip sheet from Christie's auction house

1   Jean Dubuffet, "A Word About the
     Company of Raw Art" (1948), translated
     by Carol Volk, in *Asphyxiating Culture
     and Other Writings* (New York: Four
     Walls Eight Windows, 1988), 110.

for their 2016 Outsider and Vernacular Art sale includes only one woman—the late, developmentally disabled fiber artist Judith Scott, whose star has only been ascendent over the last decade.

One self-taught female painter did recently break the one-million-dollar glass ceiling. Perhaps the most famous Outsider artist in America prior to the popularization of the term was a woman—Anna Mary Robertson "Grandma" Moses, whose orthogonally challenged pastorals were revered (equally to the works of her friend and neighbor Norman Rockwell) as a chronicles of a lost Arcadian America ↗ fig. 3. Tellingly, Ms. Moses's fame only arrived when arthritis forced her to give up embroidery and other sewing-based activities at the age of seventy-eight. We'll broach the implications of this when we dissect the Craft as Art Worm in short order. But first we should consider whether Moses's works—and by analogous legerdemain, the *Crochet Coral Reef*—may be legitimately classified as "Outsider."

Worm 1A:
Naive Folk Primitive

To those outside the world of Outsider Art, the main theme of its theoretical discourse appears to consist of internecine arguments about what exactly does or does not constitute Outsider Art—at least whenever the debate over the use of that particular umbrella term (versus Self-taught, Intuitive, Visionary, Art Brut, Folk, Naive, and Primitive) dies down.

Some purists adhere to a strict Prinzhorn-derived lineage, requiring proof of institutionalization and a notarized DSM diagnosis—in spite of the radical reorganization such criteria have undergone in the last fifty years. Others emphasize a lack of formal training, though most contemporary graduate programs hinge on idiosyncrasy and plausible de-skilling. Still others focus on aesthetic, structural, or conceptual markers—horror vacui, for example, or obsessive cataloging, or invented languages.

Moses's postwar paintings fell on the Folk, Naive, Primitive end of the spectrum, and their enormous popularity and institutional support during the ascent of Abstract Expressionism prefigured the fetishization of "authenticity" that typified the populist skepticism toward Modern Art—and has, in another incarnation—characterized the Outsider milieu ever since. But she was never in the loony bin, was not (as far as we know) channeling a Mesopotamian scribe, and in fact seems to have suffered from no remarkable psychological abnormalities.

During her lifetime (and, in fact, for the following decades up to the present time) many Art World insiders considered Moses to be little more than a reactionary shill, a folksy cartoon hillbilly tilting at the windmills of Modernism at the behest of her crypto-fascist ruling-class masters. In retrospect, however, Moses can be seen to be undermining a number of problematic aspects inherent to the Modernist agenda: she was rural as opposed to urban, from the servant class rather than the middle or upper, she was old, and she was a woman. Perhaps most subversive was her casual, unheroic, transactional attitude toward her work.

In her 2001 essay "The White-Haired Girl: A Feminist Reading" Judith E. Stein recounts how "an *Art Digest* reporter gave a charming, if simplified, account of the genesis of Moses' turn to painting, recounting her desire to give the postman 'a nice little Christmas gift.' Not only would the dear fellow appreciate a painting, concluded Grandma, but 'it was easier to make than to bake a cake over a hot stove.'"[2]

Worm the Second:
Craft as Art

Moses's easy conflation of Fine Art praxis with domestic chores (and her aforementioned unremarked-upon decades of creative needlework) brings to the surface the perennial divide between Art and Craft and the regular attempts to blur or erase this border—particularly those rooted in late twentieth century and contemporary feminism.

After the swiftly neutralized socialist efforts of William Morris and the Bauhaus, Feminist Art's redesignation of quilting, weaving, embroidery, etc. as media that had been excluded from the purview of serious art was predicated on a slightly different political ambition: to bring gender parity to the existing sphere of art history. The laudable mainstream rehabilitation of female art stars like Artemisia Gentileschi, Camille Claudel, and Frida Kahlo was a modification of the procession of Great Geniuses that made up the Western Canon. Socially oriented Feminist art strategies that deemphasized individual egos in favor of anonymous collaboration received far less attention, as the culture grew increasingly celebrity-centric.

In contrast, the Outsider agenda, informed by the anarchistic sentiments of Jean Dubuffet, saw exclusion from the mainstream as the source of its legitimacy, while adhering to the archetype of the solo-artist-as-heroic-genius. These diverging attitudes towards assimilation by the establishment were a major factor in the persistent alienation of the feminist and outsider ideologies. Central to this divide is the idea of art as the result of solitary (or solitary confinement) exploration where many are called but few are chosen, as opposed to the possibility of art as a game-like social activity where anyone can play.

2   Judith E. Stein, "The White-Haired Girl: A Feminist Reading," in Stein, *Grandma Moses in the Twenty-First Century* (New Haven: Yale University Press, 2001), citing from "Grandma Moses," *Art Digest*, October 15, 1940, https://judithestein.com/2017/12/28 /the-white-haired-girl-a-feminist -reading/.

Worm the Third:
Relational/Social Sculpture

Signal craft-based Feminist works like Judy Chicago's *Dinner Party* were emphatically built on a paradigm of communal conviviality (albeit funneled through Ms. Chicago's celebrity persona.) In the late twentieth and early twenty-first centuries, the Gee's Bend quilting community (and other groups of marginalized crafty women) emerged from the shadows to reweave the narrative of Modernist abstract design innovation ↗ fig. 4. But there's evidence to suggest that the idea of rectifying the quilting bee's role within the histories of art and civilization is putting the cart before the horse.

In *Women's Work: The First 20,000 Years*, Elizabeth Wayland Barber demonstrates how the explicitly social nature of large-scale weaving (and other textile traditions) can be deduced from archaeological evidence (Finnish bog-corpse wrappings dating to 1300 BC; archaic Greek vase paintings depicting cloth-making collectives ↗ fig. 5). There's no reason this social model can't be projected back into a prehistoric context. In a passage worth quoting at length, Barber proposes a radical reassessment of the relationship between women's work and civilization:

> We don't know how early to date this great discovery—of making string as long and as strong as needed by twisting short filaments together. But whenever it happened, it opened the door to an enormous array of new ways to save labor and improve the odds of survival, much as the harnessing of steam did for the Industrial Revolution. Soft, flexible thread of this sort is a necessary prerequisite to making woven cloth. On a far more basic level, string can be

Fig. 5 → Attributed to the Amasis Painter, detail from terracotta *lekythos* (oil flask) depicting a group of women making woolen cloth, ca. 550–530 BC. The Metropolitan Museum of Art, New York

5

used simply to tie things up—to catch, to hold, to carry. From these notions come snares and fishlines, tethers and leashes, carrying nets, handles, and packages, not to mention a way of binding objects together to form more complex tools . . . So powerful, in fact, is simple string in taming the world to human will and ingenuity that I suspect it to be the unseen weapon that allowed the human race to conquer the earth, that enabled us to move out into every econiche on the globe during the Upper Palaeolithic. We could call it the String Revolution.[3]

The Ouroboros Worm: Outsider Again

So many worms left unturned! There's the Anthropocentrism Worm: the original Great Barrier Reef may be understood as an artwork created as a nonhierarchical collaboration between polyps and algae. The Formal/Conceptual worm/s deserve an essay in themself—the *Crochet Coral Reef* model provides for exquisite mimetic replication, flamboyant psychedelic invention, and elegant minimalism, contained by a conceptual continuum that accommodates political satire and hedonistic sensuality equally.

But the worms uncanned thus far constitute a lengthy preamble to this proposition: that the *Crochet Coral Reef* is indeed "Outside"—not in the sense of being pushed to the far margins of the dominant culture and deserving a position closer to the spotlight, but in the sense that it is part of a larger, longer-lasting continuum that contains its alleged host.

3   Elizabeth Wayland Barber, *Women's Work: The First 20,000 Years* (New York and London: W. W. Norton & Company, 1994), 70.

The *Crochet Coral Reef* is a dispersed, postmodern network that organizes individual practitioners of contemplative handcrafts into real-world and virtual communities, embracing the potential of the global digital neural network, but looping back to replicate the prehistoric communal artmaking rituals of our distant ancestors ↗ fig. 6.

The default Outsider genius trope arises in direct correlation to the artist's divergence from normative consensus reality, a "coming unraveled" from the imaginational bindings of the lowest common social denominator, designating them as disassociated.

But the true object of human artmaking is human consciousness, and the basic unit of creativity is self-awareness: awareness doubled back on itself to create a knot in the undifferentiated sentience of Gaia, generating a figure-ground event. The accumulation of these knots in the collective awareness of our species is our true culture.

Loops and folds, knots and weaves, render line into something more convoluted— and stronger. The linear models for history, of language, of thought—so conducive to authoritarian supervision, to the narratives of Kings and Priests and CEOs—are curdled in the process. If we can get outside of that we (and our polyp and algae and worm cousins) may yet have a chance to survive.

Christine Wertheim

Matter, Form, and Technology: Materiality Counts

1

Fig. 1 → Orange pseudospheres
by Heather McCarren

Yarn Matters

One of the pleasures of participating in the *Crochet Coral Reef* project is to viscerally experience how much *matter* matters, how much the materials with which one works contribute to the qualities of the final object. For instance, if one uses silk yarn to make a hyperbolic form, no matter how tight the stitch or what the rate of increase, the final object will be floppy, for the qualities of silk itself do not enable its folds to stand up in stiff peaks. On the other hand, a hyperbolic made with wire will likely have some architectural strength and firmness ↗ fig. 1.

The reverse also follows, that applying the same formula—the same rate of stitch increase, the same stitch and needle size—to two *different* types of yarn, say hand-spun wool and soy yarn, produces two entirely different-looking and -feeling objects. Even the same formula applied to plarn (cut-up plastic bags) and acrylic yarn (itself a kind of plastic) produces surprisingly different effects. The item composed of plarn will be stiffer than the acrylic. Likewise, the tightness of the crochet also affects the final outcome: the tighter the stitch, the stiffer the final form and the more its ruffles will stand up in self-supporting pleats. Here we see literally how the physical properties of the materials—including hook size and stitch tightness—matter ↗ fig. 2.[1]

This issue of how the physical properties of the materials composing objects matter—including the size of the tools used to make them—is far from trivial, for it highlights questions about "knowledge" or "know-how," and how such knowledge is acquired. Specifically, crocheting corals underscores the way the expertise acquired by crochet-reefers is derived not only from the potentialities of the materials themselves, but also through the reefers' interactions with these. For through the practice of crafting—handy interactions with materials—reefers come to discover, learn, understand, and remember a great deal, both about how materials behave and how forms can develop through the complex interactions between the various material components: yarn type, hook size, stitch rate, tightness of technical execution, and so on. However, this understanding is acquired, not through readings books, but through the activity of *doing* or making itself, a process known as "acquiring a skill." The point is that practical skills are infused with know-how, that is, knowledge and information.

In other words, the *Crochet Coral Reef* project demonstrates what scholars are now beginning to highlight: that the generation and transmission of knowledge do not consist solely in the production and communication of "pure" information and ideas, and are not passed on only through the medium of symbols and words. They also require processes of material-making and physical interactions with material substances. This idea flies in the face of Western assumptions about understanding, where it has long been held that knowledge is primarily composed of, and generated by forms and ideas, or what we today call "information."

1   Mathematicians are now exploring the way hyperbolic forms are altered by their embeddings in different materials

From genes to digital technologies, and even the string-figurings of ancient Andean *khipu,* we are told, information provides the blueprint for phenomena, with the matter in which this is instantiated being seen as secondary. Here is the metaphysics of *The Matrix,* a philosophical viewpoint echoed in countless science fiction films and novels.

But, while wrapped in the splendors of computer graphics, this vision simply recapitulates Plato's age-old argument that the "true" reality—accessible only to "enlightened" souls—is the realm of Ideas or Forms. In Plato's universe there were three orders of phenomena: the Ideal, the Physical, and the Imagined. Take for example, a rose. For Plato, there are three roses. First and most "real" is the Ideal Rose, the pure "form" or idea of a "perfect" rose. Second is any actual physically incarnated rose. But this material rose is, for Plato, merely a degraded *copy* of its Ideal. Lastly, there are images—pictures, poems, or other *descriptions* of roses— that are copies of a copy of the original Ideal. In Plato's hierarchical schema the most "real" rose is the Ideal one, not the physically incarnated version, which again is merely a copy.

In the digital age we no longer worry if experience involves "copies"—indeed, our contemporary world is increasingly filled with images that have no "originals" at all, such as virtual-reality games, photoshopped pictures, and fantasy television shows. But for Plato, such horrors were a species of spiritual sin leading the soul ever further from its true home in the realm of Ideas and Forms. The word he used to describe such horrors was "simulacra," a term of specific disdain. Today we prefer the term "information" to "form," but it is essentially the same idea, for this contemporary buzzword simply repeats the Platonic perspective that ideas, forms, or codes literally in-form the world, with matter again conceived as a mere substance into which information or data impresses itself. Known technically as *formalism,* this idealistic perspective has dominated the Western world for the past two thousand years.

Embedded in this viewpoint is also a gender dimension, for in the Western mindset, ideas, form, and information have been intrinsically affiliated with masculinity, while matter and substance have long been coded as feminine. Plato, again, is one origin for this division. In Platonic thought the male seed provides all the necessary information for creating a human life while the female seed contributes only the matter or clay in which this form takes root. Here the mother is nothing but a vessel in which the father implants the blueprint and spark for a new being.[2] Plato followed other Greek philosophers in associating *mind* with masculinity and placing women on the other end of a spectrum as intrinsically *un*-minded. Where men could aspire to understand the realm of higher Ideals, women were seen as forever grounded in the slothful pull of their maternal substance and shut out of *understanding* in all its "true" forms, including science and mathematics.

2 Plato, *Timaeus.*

Fig. 2 → One of a series of tiny beaded hyperbolic planes by Rebecca Peapples. The crochet algorithm is translated into a beading stitch.

2

Reacting against these dualisms, the Enlightenment philosopher Baruch Spinoza refused the divides between matter and form, body, and mind. Instead, for Spinoza, "the capacity of the body is mirrored in the capacity of the mind."[3] Furthermore, for him, "the more complex the mechanisms of the body, the more complex the mechanisms of thought in the mind."[4] As Eva Perez de Vega has argued, one could conclude from this "that a more complex body is a more complex mind. In other words, the more the body is capable of, the more the mind is also capable of."[5] While not claiming the superiority of one type of body over another, de Vega is slyly tempted to propose, not wholly ironically, that "female bodies are more complex, and capable of more complex functions than are male bodies," because, "due to female reproductive organs, the female body is inherently . . . capable of *doing much more.*"[6] Taken seriously, this line of reasoning could overturn the Platonic tradition, which, it might be argued, has always been a reactive defense against Western men's sense of inferiority in the face of female fecundity, the capacity of the female body to materially *do* something. Seen from this perspective, formalism in its totality looks much like a masculine attempt to downplay female-coded modes of practical and material understanding and know-how.

The same could be said of contemporary attitudes to computers, which despite a geeky focus on data and "pure" information, always require some kind of material hardware as support—screens, consoles, server banks, and the microchips without which none of this could function. Not to mention the energy needed to power them, which is itself a physical stream of electrons driven by vast material power plants fueled by substances such as coal and oil, or even sunlight, itself a stream of photons. All of which suggests, again, that information is *not* the only, or most "true" aspect of reality. Matter also counts. From this perspective, the idea of a pure immaterialized Ideal is nothing more than a fiction. Today, scholars in

3   Eva Perez de Vega, "Spinoza and Feminism Question the Structures of Domination: Is the Mind-Body Problem a Gender Problem?," Public Seminar, April 30, 2018, https://publicseminar .org/2018/04/spinoza-and-feminism -question-the-structures-of-domination/ (accessed October 8, 2021).

4   De Vega, "Spinoza and Feminism."

5   De Vega.

6   De Vega.

a plethora of fields are rethinking the formalist perspective by focusing on the contributions that matter makes *as* matter.[7]

Ironically, one effect of this reassessment of matter's contribution, is a reappraisal of what should constitute academic work itself. Some scholars now even argue that "research" should no longer be conducted via purely textual and linguistic means—practices of supposedly pure ideas. In this newly emergent way of seeing, research also includes embodied, performative material and gestural methods involving bodies interacting with one another, and with other material forms across real time and space. By this means, it is argued, wholly new kinds of ideas and concepts will emerge. Examples of this approach include data-visualization methods, and multimedia modes entwining images with text.[8] I would argue that psychotherapeutic practices and legal disputes also fall into this category, for these too involve inquiry, problem-solving, and knowledge-generation through inter-actions between speaking-bodies in real space-time. Some researchers in Canada have even set up a *Senselab* where scholars dance and move while they listen and speak.[9] Perhaps the most interesting developments in this new movement are to be found in recent changes in thinking about early human technology.

Technology in History

As many scholars argue today, "technology" is not confined to the stuff with elec-tricity whizzing through it or with microchips at its core. Technology includes all forms of doing involving developed "techniques" that extend beings' capacities to perform otherwise difficult or impossible tasks. Technology, we could say, is prosthetics: prosthetics of both mind and body. A stick used to ferret insects out of a nest (in order to eat them) is a technology. Memorizing a song is also a tech-nology, as is tying knots. As a complex form of knot-tying, *crochet* is a technol-ogy, even a digital technology, for though there is no electricity involved, crochet employs patterns encrypted in symbolic codes, just like computer programs.[10] In this prosthetic sense, chimpanzees and some other species are technological animals, for they too use tools and songs to extend their capacities. And some of these species even pass their know-how on from generation to generation. But humans seem to have an even more extended prosthetic capacity that enables us to develop acquired skills to a degree not seen in other species, however intelligent these may otherwise be. The question is, how did these skills initially develop in our early ancestors?

Until recently, it had been thought that when proto-humans began making sharp-pointed stone arrowheads, as opposed to simply chipping away at rocks, they must have had a predetermined idea of what they were aiming at. In other words, before the material object appeared, there had to have been an *Idea* of it, a mental image of its Form, in the mind. This view, known as "representationalism," shows how deep

7   Rebekah Sheldon, "Form/Matter/ Chora: Object-Oriented Ontology and Feminist New Materialism," in Richard Grusin, ed., *The Nonhuman Turn* (Minneapolis: University of Minnesota Press, 2015). See also Humboldt Univer-sity, Berlin, research cluster, "Matters of Activity, https://www.matters -of-activity.de/en/research/projects /123/symbolic-material (accessed October 8, 2021).

8   "Matters of Activity."

9   See www.senselab.ca/wp2/about/ and the University of Victoria's Maker Lab.

10   See Margaret Wertheim's essay on pages 70–79 and Kayleigh C. Perkov's essay on pages 20–27 in this catalog.

Fig. 4 → *Pod World—Hyperbolic* with corals by Christine Wertheim, Margaret Wertheim, Anitra Menning, and Heather McCarren. Installation view, 58th Venice Biennale, 2019

4

Platonic thinking goes in the Western world. Today archeologists are questioning this assumption, proposing that it was *not* necessary to have a *preformed idea* of the object-aim in order to produce a stone with a point at one specific place. Now, a new school of "relational-material-archeology" argues that the hand's interaction with the stone is at least partially guided by the properties of the stone itself, to chip in certain directions.[11] This does not mean that the stone has intentions or will. But it does mean that potentialities inherent in the stone's material properties play a role in the production of the stone axe, at least in the early stages of its development.[12] The consequence of this perspective is that knowledge-generation is now understood as emerging in part from interactive material processes in which no predetermined ideas, images, concepts, or forms need be present.

Scholars of early human technology tend to focus on technologies we code as masculine, such as stone craft. However, sometime long-ago humans—or perhaps even prehumans—also experienced a revolution when string or yarn was discovered or invented. The simple observation that twisting short fibers together could produce long, strong cords enabled our ancestors to do previously unimaginable things.[13] With string, nets, and other fiber-based constructions, we could now carry and move large quantities of stuff, corral fish, and weave cloth, enabling societies to bond in new ways, through new collective tasks. Fishermen, weavers, vegetable-gathers, and mothers with babies were now bound by networks of knots. Crochet too can be seen as a networking of knot.[14] The act of tying a knot was thus as important as constructing a stone blade, and, if the material archeologists are correct, probably also developed through long improvisational handlings of fibrous materials.[15]

Similarly, we crochet-reefers do not always begin with predetermined ideas in mind. Often, we just let interactions between hand, yarn, and hook guide the development of the work, and thus its final "form," which can, because of this, end up quite surprising. Thus, while learning specific patterns or algorithms from *one another* is an important part of the project's evolution, innovation in the shape of *un*-foreseen developments due to the selection of new materials or the choice of new stitch styles, are also unquestionably a factor in much of the *Reef's* ongoing, ever-expanding diversity. Likewise, the knowledge and know-how the project generates are rooted as much in our interactive material explorations as in the formalities of the patterns we encode.

11 Lambros Malafouris, *How Things Shape the Mind: A Theory of Material Engagement* (Cambridge, MA: MIT Press, 2018).

12 Clearly here the *type* of stone is crucial. Perhaps if Africa had not been abundant in certain stone-types, this form of toolmaking might not have evolved, though others surely would (as was the case in Indigenous Australia).

13 Elizabeth Wayland Barber, *Women's Work: The First 20,000 Years—Women, Cloth, and Society in Early Times* (New York: W. W. Norton & Company, 1995). See also Doug Harvey's essay on pages 54–61 of this catalog.

14 Strictly speaking, a piece of crochet, or knitting, is simply a complex series of slipknots. Not until it is tied off at the end does it technically become a *mathematical* knot. But this does not undermine the overall point about the significance of such techniques in human history.

15 Simian-scientists have discovered that some apes can teach themselves to tie knots, and perhaps even pass the skill on to their children. Perhaps *Planet of the Apes* is not as far-fetched as it might appear?

Margaret Wertheim

Crochet Codes and a Crafty DNA

1

Fig. 1 → Vintage lace doily

In the Information Age we have been taught to think of coding as a symbolic apparatus aimed at the disembodied mind, yet female crafters have been deploying codes for centuries. As a technology, crochet precedes computing in its use of codes and algorithmic processes to generate programmed outcomes. Indeed, crafts such as crochet, knitting, basketry, and weaving were the original *digital* technologies—*technes* created by digits—and it is one of the ironies of the computer age that the "digital" has come to connote disembodiment and divorce from the material domain when the term was derived from our hands. History records this linkage in the punch cards used for early computers that elaborated on a system developed to automate looms. In crafts we continue to witness the power of visual codes and the ability to read, enact, transform, and engage with information via our corporeal beings.

2

Crochet doily patterns, with their diatom-like graphics, are examples of a spatialized code a crafter can read through her eyes ↗ fig. 2. Each mark or string of symbols represents a set of stitches to be performed, making these images visual algorithms.[1] Beginning at the center and following the code described by gradually spiraling out, the crocheter performs the recipe it describes with her fingers, using yarn as a medium to bring the instructions into material form as a piece of fiber art.

A crafty cryptology is manifest here, for each of these diagrams is an *icon* conveying structural information about a form to be fabricated in thread. But crochet actually encompasses two distinct kinds of code. In addition to the visual one is an *alphabetic* code, with each stitch type described by groups of letters—*ch* for "chain," *sc* for "single crochet," *dc* for "double crochet," and so on. This dialect of the digits is another way of representing patterns, as in the one for a ruffled doily ↗ fig. 3.[2]

1 I am indebted to Crochet Coral Reef contributor Sarah Simons for scanning these images of traditional doily patterns from old pattern books. An animation of these forms is included in the exhibition.

2 Images of crochet pattern and finished doily, from the magazine *Ruffled Doilies and the Pansy* Doily, Star Book 59 (New York: American Thread Company, Inc., 1948).

Fig. 3 → Alphabetic doily pattern, from *Ruffled
Doilies and the Pansy Doily*, Star Book No. 59,
The American Thread Company, Inc., 1948

Fig. 4 → Hyperbolic doily is the final
form of the pattern on this page, after the
piece has been starched and ironed

Double Ruffle No. 5901

(Illustrated on Front Cover)

s c in center s c of next double knot st, repeat from * 3 times, single knot st, 1 d c in each of the next 2 d c, repeat from ** all around ending row with single knot st, s c in center s c of next double knot st, * double knot st, s c in center s c of next double knot st, repeat from * 3 times, single knot st, join.

15th Row. Double knot st, skip the single knot st, s c in center s c of next double knot st, * double knot st, s c in center s c of next double knot st, repeat from * twice, double knot st, skip the single knot st, s c in next d c, repeat from beginning all around.

16th Row. Sl st to center of next double knot st. * work a double knot st, s c in center s c of next double knot st, repeat from * all around.

17th Row. Sl st to center of next knot st, * ch 6, s c in center s c of next double knot st, repeat from * all around ending row with ch 3, d c in sl st, this brings thread in position for next row (70 loops).

18th Row. Ch 8, d c in next loop, * ch 5, d c in next loop, repeat from * all around, ch 5, join in 3rd st of ch.

29th Row. Attach thread in 3rd loop to left of joining of last row, ch 3, 5 d c in same loop, * ch 4, s c in next loop, ch 5, d c in next loop, ch 5, s c in next loop, ch 4, 6 d c in next loop, repeat from * all around ending row to correspond, join.

30th Row. Ch 3, 1 d c in each of the next 4 d c. * ch 4, d c in next s c, ch 4, s c in next loop, s c in next d c, s c in next loop, ch 4, d c in next s c, ch 4, 1 d c in each of the next 5 d c, repeat from * all around ending row to correspond, join.

31st Row. Ch 3, 1 d c in each of the next 3 d c, * ch 4, s c in next loop, 1 s c in next d c, s c in next loop, ch 4, 1 d c in center s c of next s c group, ch 4, s c in next loop, s c in next d c, s c in next loop, ch 4, 1 d c in each of the next 4 d c, repeat from * all around ending row to correspond, join.

32nd Row. Ch 3, 1 d c in each of the next 2 d c, * ch 5, d c in center s c of next s c group, ch 4, s c in next loop, s c in next d c, s c in next loop, ch 4, d c in center s c of next s c group, ch 5, 1 d c in each of the next 3 d c, repeat from * all around ending row to correspond, join.

3

Fig. 5 → Diagrammatic crochet
pattern for a star-shaped doily

Alphabetic crochet patterns like this are a craft equivalent of computer programs. Both employ a coded lexicon to indicate specific steps, and both utilize "subroutines," small programs-within-programs that get called on as repeats. (Such subroutines are indicated in the pattern above by an asterisk.) Yet for all the power of alphabetic patterns, the *graphic* variety has added virtues. From the alphabetic pattern ↗ fig. 3, it's hard to imagine the object being created until it emerges in your hands—who but an expert crafter would recognize the remarkable form in the next image as the result of this code?

With a diagrammatic pattern one knows from the start the configuration it will produce, for the visual graphology presents a one-to-one correspondence with the structural components of the form. Consider the pattern for a star-shaped doily ↗ fig. 5. Here, loops represent chains and struts represent single, double, triple, and half crochet stitches. One grasps from the image the holistic nature of the form being modeled in a way an alphabetic pattern cannot convey.

5

Termed "iconic" by the pioneering nineteenth-century mathematician Charles Sanders Pierce, such visual modes of conveying information were to him the superior form of signification.[3] Pierce believed practitioners of all sciences, including mathematics, should strive to develop the most iconic notations for representing knowledge, and he famously developed graphical systems to describe the logic underlying computing. Among his inspirations were electrical circuit diagrams that lay out component parts much like doily patterns and assist engineers to generate equations ↗ fig. 6. Contemporary icons also include subway maps such as the one for the London Underground, a classic example of twentieth-century informatic design that condenses a complex citywide network into a digestible image. In all these cases, diagrams depict a set of relationships between elements in space capturing the essence of their topological arrangements. Drawings serve here not as a means for personal expression but as a technology for visualizing a logic of spatial relations—they become, so to speak, devices to *think with*.

In considering modes of representation Pierce was particularly drawn to the science of chemistry, which, also akin to crochet, has an alphabetic and a graphic

3   Albert Atkin, "Pierce's Theory of Signs," in The Stanford Encyclopedia of Philosophy, ed. Edward N. Zalta (Stanford: Metaphysics Research Lab, Stanford University, 2010).

Fig. 6 → Electrical circuit diagram   Fig. 7 → Graphic representation of the anticancer drug Taxol

6

7

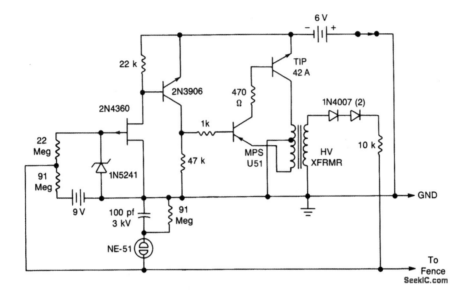

mode for describing the structures of molecules and their chemical interactions. Although crochet and chemistry might at first appear very distant subjects—one affiliated with home and hearth, the other evoking antiseptic "scientific" spaces— both activities can be denoted by almost parallel modes of representation, making crochet patterns a near-perfect analog for the language of chemical forms.

Molecules, too, can be conveyed by a lexical grammar of letters and numbers and by illustrative images. Take the case of benzene, an important molecule composed of six carbon atoms and six hydrogens. Written alphabetically, benzene's chemical formula is C_6H_6 ↗ fig. 8.

As the study of atomic assemblages, chemistry is combinatoric: while there are only a hundred or so atoms, these can be arranged in an infinite variety of ways. Not everything is possible, however—laws and patterns and regularities assert themselves. In order to understand atomic relationships, graphical notation gives chemists insights into the arrangement of atoms in space that turn out to be an essential feature of many molecular forms not easily grasped by their alphabetic description. Once more a visual code enables us to *see* at a glance the holistic nature of a molecule. At the heart of benzene, above, is a hexagonal structure called an "aromatic ring," composed of six connected carbons. Such rings appear throughout the realm of "organic" chemistry underlying life, and are also found in myriad synthetic products. According to a 1988 study, two thirds of *all* chemicals on the American Chemical Society's official list contain at least one benzene ring.[4] Although benzene by itself is a carcinogen, the anticancer drug Taxol contains three of its rings, pointing to the powerful role these structures play in animal physiology ↗ fig. 7.

Kevlar, a fiber that can be spun into strands stronger than steel and used in bicycle tires and bulletproof vests, consists of long molecular chains of interconnected aromatic rings joined by other atoms in a lace-like net. As with crochet patterns, in chemical graphology specific groupings of rings have names and functions that a trained chemist can interpret through her eyes ↗ fig. 9.

4   Malcolm W. Browne, "A Pervasive Molecule Is Captured in a Photograph, *New York Times, August 16, 1988,* https://www.nytimes.com/1988/08/16 /science/a-pervasive-molecule-is -captured-in-a-photograph.html (accessed October 6, 2021).

Fig. 9 → Graphic representation of Kevlar. Written out alphabetically, the chemical formula for Kevlar is [-CO-C$_6$H$_4$-CO-NH-C$_6$H$_4$-NH-].

Such diagrams highlight another feature shared by chemistry and crochet and by their respective notations; that although all complex arrangements are composed from a finite set of primitives—atoms or stitches—in both realms, clusters of these elements appear again and again as larger stable structures. These units often acquire names of their own. Chemistry has its aromatic rings, its hydroxyl groups, and so on. In crochet, popcorns, picots, bullions, and bobbles are motifs found in patterns for doilies, edgings, blankets, and wedding gowns. This phenomenon of atomic clustering also underpins the language or code of DNA.

Where digital computers operate on a *binary* code, DNA's code is *quaternary* with four basic "letters." In the formalities of computing, digital *bits* are grouped into *bytes*—usually of eight or sixteen bits—so, also, DNA letters group into clusters, this time of three each, called "codons." Strings of codons spell out the messages for building the proteins living things are made of. However, if this code was always perfectly reproduced stasis would settle on the Earth, locking life into a groove with no new formations. The virtue of DNA lies in its propensity for *imperfect* reproduction. When cells holding DNA replicate, malfunctions can occur: here or there a letter is changed. Perhaps one is deleted, or something new gets added in. Such "mistakes" are among the driving factors of *evolution* as deviations at the molecular level cause mutations in the physiology of organisms leading to

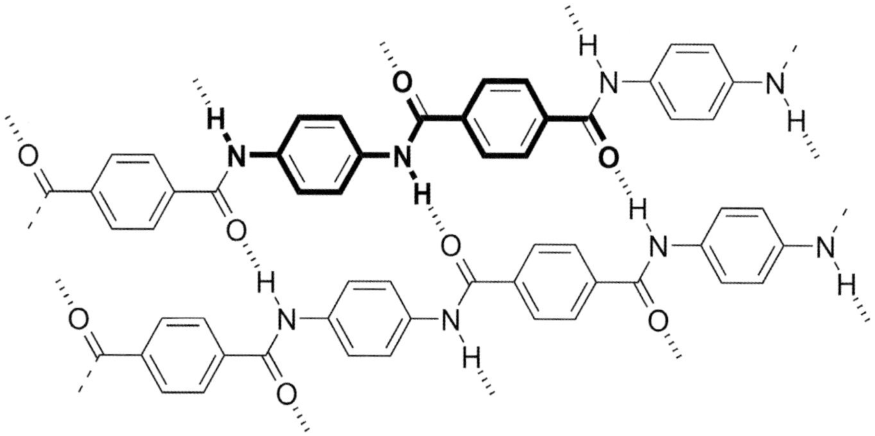

9

"This is where the *Crochet Coral Reef* recapitulates life on Earth, for we crochet-reefers also begin with simple seeds that gradually evolve via deviations into more complex forms. Everyone who comes to the project starts with the kernel of a basic algorithm . . ."

diversity, and ultimately to the taxonomic variety Ernst Haeckel called the "tree of life"—an evocative if controversial phrase. Life, then, is poised at the boundary of continuity and change. While the core of our code stays stable—we humans share ninety-eight to ninety-nine percent of our DNA with chimpanzees and some percentage with lettuce—speciation results from aberrations randomly injected into the system.[5] As theorized by the Chilean biologist-philosopher Francisco Varela, life can be characterized as a balance between that which endures and that which transforms.[6]

This is where the *Crochet Coral Reef* recapitulates life on Earth, for we crochet-reefers also begin with simple seeds that gradually evolve via deviations into more complex forms. Everyone who comes to the project starts with the kernel of a basic algorithm that generates a perfect "hyperbolic" shape, very much like the ruffled doily of ↗ fig. 4. *Crochet 'n' stitches, increase one stitch; repeat ad infinitum,* is our starting recipe; and by following this process the crafter creates a mathematically accurate hyperbolic surface.[7] Yet these forms—precise, even, symmetrical—are the antithesis of living things, for life is never perfect in the Platonist sense and living things are never quite regular. The move into "imperfection" also sparks the *Reef* project to "life" hefting it from the domain of geometric precision into a kind of fiberized organicism. Having learned the basic hyperbolic technique, each crafter is free to inject their own deviations; to add to the code, or change it here and there, as occurs in the evolution of living things. We too, *queer* the code. "Iterate, deviate, innovate" has been the motto of the project. What is it *you* can imagine that no one else has done before? Thus, each maker can invent new branches on a crochet "tree of life." As Earthly organisms accrete variations, so our crochet reef community has accreted a library of pattern formations, bringing into being a wooly taxonomy of crochet coral "species." Working with codes, we *reefers* together craft ever-more diverse string figures, generating a simulacrum of both life and evolution that results in a visionary, yarn-based ecology.

5   See "Humans and Chimpanzees Share 99% of the Same DNA," Swiss Institute of January 18, 2021,Genetic Literacy Project, https://geneticliteracyproject .org/2021/01/18/humans-and-chimpan zees-share-99-of-the-same-dna-this-is -the-1-difference/ (accessed September 17, 2021); and "Shared Human/ Lettuce DNA," December 31, 2008, AskMetaFilter https://ask.metafilter.com /110434/Shared-humanlettuce-DNA (accessed September 17, 2021). Exactly how much DNA humans share with other organisms is much debated because it depends on what kinds of DNA one counts. Genes only constitute part of our DNA. There is also "junk DNA," whose function isn't often known. The further removed we are from an organism in evolutionary history, the more complex the question becomes.

6   Humberto R. Maturana and Francisco J. Varela, *Autopoiesis and Cognition: The Realization of the Living, Boston Studies in the Philosophy of Science* 42, ed. Robert S. Cohen and Marx W. Wartofsky (Dordrecht, Holland, and Boston: Reidel Publishing, 1980).

7   See Margaret Wertheim's essay "A Field Guide to Hyperbolic Space," on pages 80–89 in this catalog, for more about these shapes and their crochet incarnation.

Pages 78–79: Vintage plastic and lace doilies in various sizes. The red tatted doily (opposite page, bottom right) is by *Föhr Satellite Reef* contributor Gertrud von Krichau-Anderssen. The doily on the top right on this page is loaned by Roxanne Steinberg. All others are from the collection of the Institute For Figuring.

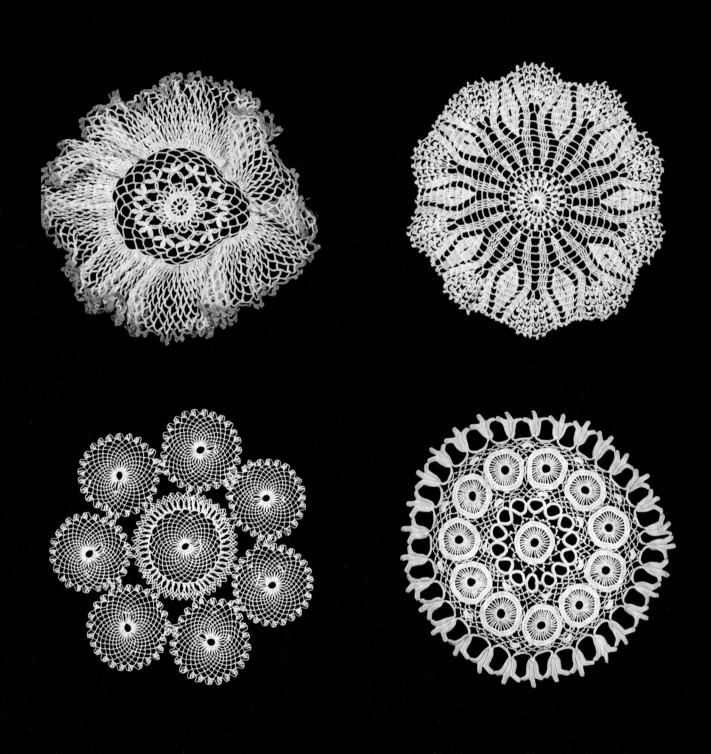

Margaret Wertheim

A Field Guide to Hyperbolic Space

1

Fig. 1 → Crochet hyperbolic
plane by Anitra Menning

Fig. 2 → M.C. Escher, *Circle Limit IV (Heaven and Hell)*, woodcut, printed from two blocks, July 1960

"For God's sake, please give it up. Fear it no less than the sensual passions, because it, too, may take up all your time and deprive you of your health, peace of mind and happiness in life."

Farkas Wolfgang Bolyai (1775–1856)

We have built a world of rectilinearity. The rooms we inhabit, the skyscrapers we work in, and the grid-like arrangement of our streets speak to us in straight lines. Yet outside our boxes the natural world teems with swooping, curling, and crenellated forms, from the fluted surfaces of lettuce leaves and fungi to the frilled skirts of nudibranchs and the animal undulations of sea slugs. We have learned to play by Euclidean rules because two thousand years of geometrical training have engraved the grid in our minds. But in the early nineteenth century, mathematicians became aware of a space in which lines cavorted in aberrant formations, suggesting the existence of a new geometry.

To all at the time *hyperbolic* space seemed pathological for it contravened the dictates of Euclid, overthrowing millennia of mathematical wisdom and offending common sense. "I fear the howl of the Boeotians, if I make my discoveries known," wrote Carl Friedrich Gauss, the "prince of mathematicians." A century later, the Dutch artist M. C. Escher propelled hyperbolic space into the cultural zeitgeist with his *Circle Limit* series of etchings, tessellating birds and fishes or angles and demons to demonstrate in graphic play the superabundant structure hidden within this geometry ↗ fig. 2.

2

Characterized by an almost organic excess, hyperbolic space resembles nothing so much as a sea creature. Indeed, eons before the dawning of mathematical awareness in the human mind, nature had exploited this form throughout the vegetable and marine kingdoms. The human discovery of hyperbolic space initiated the field of *non-Euclidean* geometry and opened our eyes to the possibility that cosmic space itself may have another structure than the Cartesian box of Newtonian science. Though it had long been thought that the space of our universe must conform to Euclid's ideals, data now coming from far-off galaxies suggests the cosmological whole may be a hyperbolic form.

This is a shortened version of my book *A Field Guide to Hyperbolic Space: An Exploration of the Intersection of Higher Geometry and Feminine Handcraft* (Los Angeles: Institute For Figuring, 2007).

3   4

At the heart of our inquiry is the concept of straightness: what exactly does it mean
to talk about a "straight line" and how do such "objects" relate to one another? If
straightness at first seems obvious, it turns out to be a subtle and elastic concept.
To understand what's at stake we must go back to Euclid and the original axioms
of geometry, long regarded in Western philosophy as a model for reason itself.
Euclid based his mathematical system on five supposedly self-evident propositions.
The first four seem uncontroversial, in effect defining a point, a line, a circle, and a
right angle. While the fifth axiom also sounds reasonable, mathematicians always
approached it with caution. It defines the condition for "parallel" lines. Modern
understanding of this so-called parallel postulate describes it as follows: take a
line, and draw a point outside this line ↗ fig. 3.

Now consider how many other lines we can draw through the point that never
meet the original line. All lines must be straight. Our apprehension is that the
answer is one—a so-called parallel—for every other line would slant and thus
intersect the first ↗ fig. 4.

83

Fig. 5 → What are straight lines on
the curved surface of a sphere?

Fig. 6 → Straight lines on
a sphere are great circles

5

6

For an *axiom,* however, this seems unduly complex. If it is true, mathematicians speculated they should be able to prove it from the other simpler axioms. That there is any issue here is hinted at by another geometric form we all know well—the surface of the Earth. Take a sphere and repeat the exercise. Again, we ask the question: if I draw a straight line on this surface and a point outside the line, how many straight lines can I draw through the point that *never* meet the original line ↗ fig. 5 ?

A conundrum confronts us here: what does it mean to talk about a straight line on a curved surface? Mathematicians spent centuries articulating their answer: On curved surfaces straight lines can be generalized into the concept of a *geodesic,* which always trace the shortest possible path between any two points. On the surface of a sphere geodesics are *great circles*, like the Equator or lines of longitude dividing the Earth into two equal parts ↗ fig. 6. Airlines use geodesics when charting international flight paths. Though these *look* curved on flat maps in airline magazines, they are "straight" in relation to the globe itself, and millions of dollars in jet fuel is saved by this understanding. Math meets economic imperative.

7

Returning to our original question, we ask about the relationship between a straight line on the sphere and other lines we may draw through an external point. Knowledge about the Earth's surface should lead us to the answer, for here *all* great circles intersect one another—think of the lines of longitude crossing the equator and also one another at the poles. Thus, on a sphere there are no "straight" lines that never meet the original line ↗ <u>fig. 7</u>.

Euclid's postulate states there could not be *more than* one; and so, the proposition still holds. Yet can we be sure there aren't other surfaces in which *two or more* parallels might co-exist?

That *one* might not be the limit struck moral outrage in the hearts of mathematicians who did their best for two thousand years to show how Euclid must be right. In the eighteenth century, the Jesuit mathematician Girolamo Saccheri devoted his life to the task yet was unable to find any logical reason why this limit could not be exceeded. Even Gauss could find no reason and chose to be silent rather than publish his heretical findings. Finally, two mathematicians converged on the same result. In Hungary in 1823 János Boylai wrote to his father with the news:

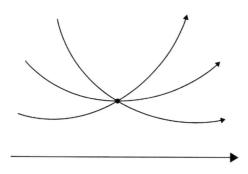

8

"I have created a new and different world," while in Russia, Nikolai Lobachevsky was visited by the same angel of insight. Whatever the insult to common sense, another alternative to Euclid had to be admitted into the domain of geometrical sense.

Mathematicians were compelled to accept that there exists a surface in which given a line and a point outside the line, there are an *infinite* number of other straight lines that intersect the point yet never meet the original line. As a homage to this excess of parallels, they named this surface the *hyperbolic* plane ↗ fig. 8.

Very likely the reader is objecting that in the image above the lines are curved. However, they only *look* curved because we are trying to project them onto a flat plane. From the point of view of a being *within* the space they are straight. We can think of this analogously to the sphere, where, as we saw above, straight lines also look curved in flat-map projections. Only from *outside* the sphere do they *appear* curved. The proof you are following a straight line on a curved surface is that you are traversing the shortest possible distance. Straightness thus becomes a relational concept, always mapping minimal distance between points.

Fig. 9 → Poincare disc model
of hyperbolic plane

9

Yet it is one thing to prove that some mathematical object exists, it's quite another to understand what it is. Like the blind man and the elephant, hyperbolic space has many different guises depending how we approach it. One way of cognizing this structure was discovered at the end of the nineteenth century by Henri Poincaré, the father of topology. In the Poincaré disk model of hyperbolic geometry, the entire space is inscribed inside a disk. In reality the hyperbolic plane, like the Euclidean plane, is infinite; but in order to *represent* it within a Euclidean framework compromises are needed, and Poincare's compromise was to represent *angles* truly while distorting *scales* ↗ <u>fig. 9</u>.

Despite appearances in this diagram the triangular shaped areas are all the same size. Though they seem to us to be decreasing in scale as we move toward the perimeter, *within* the space itself they are equal, and the boundary of the circle is always infinitely far away. In his book *Science and Hypothesis* (1902), Poincaré wrote of this model as an imaginary universe. To us as *external* observers of this apparently finite bubble-world, the inhabitants of the space appear to shrink as they approach the perimeter. They however, embedded *within* the space, feel no such effect. As far as they are concerned, they live in an infinite non-diminishing world. Only we, from an *outside* perspective, see their proportions fading away to nothingness. Mathematicians characterize this as a difference between an *intrinsic* and *extrinsic* view.

Poincaré's disk model entered the cultural lexicon with Escher, who studied the concept under the tutelage of the geometer Donald Coxeter and rendered it into patterns of triangles, hexagons, octagons, and squares played out by beasts and fantasy creatures. Escher's images introduce an elegant lesson: with its density of parallels, hyperbolic space can be filled with a much richer variety of tiling patterns than the Euclidean plane. Escher was also inspired by the Moorish patterns he encountered at the Alhambra palace in Spain. If, as the masters of Islamic tiling believed, that repeated patterns connote the divine, then Heaven might just be a hyperbolic space.

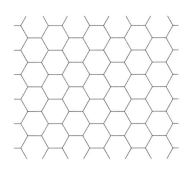

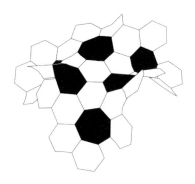

10   11   12

For all the beauty of the Poincaré disk model, however, it obscures as much as it reveals. Can we define a model of hyperbolic space that speaks more directly to our physical intuitions? For a long time, mathematicians thought this too may be impossible, yet tiling patterns offer another conduit of insight. We all know a bathroom floor can be tiled with hexagons, filling the space completely ↗ fig. 10. If we want to tile the surface of a sphere, however, we have to replace some of the (six-sided) hexagons with (five-sided) pentagons. The resulting form is a soccer ball—not quite a sphere, but a nice approximation. By *taking away* some sides we have produced a *smaller* and finite form ↗ fig. 11. To tessellate the hyperbolic plane, we make the opposite move, replacing some of the hexagons with (seven-sided) heptagons. *Adding in* sides here, the surface opens out to an infinite, excessive, ruffled shape with much *more* surface than a Euclidean plane ↗ fig. 12.

Just this kind of ruffling is endemic in the organic world—we see it in lettuce leaves and kales, corals, kelps, sea sponges, and nudibranchs, which are biological manifestations of a surface human mathematicians long thought to be impossible. Unimpeded by Euclid's dictates, invertebrates have been getting on with it for hundreds of millions of years. Which raises the question of what does it mean to "know" hyperbolic geometry? Does a sea slug, with its frills, understand hyperbolic space? I would argue that it does. To make a form in the fibers of one's being is a kind of *embodied* knowing and we can theorize that realizations of mathematical structures are a form of cognition. This gets us away from the normative view of mathematics as a purely symbolic system, comprehendible only through writing and thinking with symbols and equations. I want to argue that hyperbolic geometry, with its pedigree in the organic realm, suggests an alternative way of think about math, giving us a way of seeing it as something that cannot only be written down, but also *played out*, by and in material systems ↗ fig. 13.

One way of playing out hyperbolic forms is to crochet them. This innovation was discovered by Dr. Daina Taimina while trying to assist her geometer-husband at

Cornell University to introduce the subject to his mathematics students. Growing up as a crafter, Taimina had encountered ruffles in knitting and crochet, and she came to understand that a process of increasing stitches could emulate the excess surface characteristic of hyperbolic forms. Adding stitches is an analog of the process we saw above of adding sides to the hexagons; in both instances we force a surface to increase beyond Euclidean norms by packing in *more* elements than flatness can contain. At first, Taimina made one with knitting. But too many stitches accumulate on the needles, and she switched to crochet, whose one-stitch-at-a-time mechanics lends itself perfectly to fabrication of these unruly shapes.[1]

Human hands are brilliant manipulation machines and by following a simple algorithm anyone can learn to crochet hyperbolic forms in minutes. *Crochet 'n' stitches then increase one stitch; repeat ad infinitum*—this is the recipe we use. Rather like a fractal growing, as one iterates these steps, a frilly form begins to take shape that resembles the crenellated surfaces seen in so many natural organisms. Craft thus becomes a mechanism for exploring branches of both geometry and biology. Indeed, we may say that in crafting hyperbolic surfaces we crochet-reefers are enacting a kind of wooly biology ↗ fig. 14.

14

While pure hyperbolic surfaces belong to a different branch of geometry than fractals, the *iterative* nature of craft practices enables us to translate the mathematical ideal of a hyperbolic form into the physical reality of a material object. In effect, the stringy nature of yarn forms a bridge between the *discrete* and *continuous* realms conjoining thousands of individual stitches into a sheet-like continuum. From the point of view of "pure mathematics" this is an illegitimate move, which is perhaps one reason why it took an outsider—and a woman—to realize how this could be done. And so, I ask again: what does it mean to *know* hyperbolic geometry? In crafting these surfaces, women crocheting hyperbolic corals are actively exploring non-Euclidean space; and the *Crochet Coral Reef* project, which is an exercise in the possibilities of such forms, is a collective global experiment in applied mathematics.

1 Knitting is an innately Euclidean medium, because the knitter generates row upon row of linked lock-step lines. One can also crochet Euclidean surfaces—think of a granny-square blanket—however there is nothing innate about this, and crochet lends itself just as easily to the generation of non-Euclidean forms. This superior geometric freedom is enabled by the fact that when crocheting, the crafter is always working at a single point and is thus at greater liberty to go in any direction they choose, making crochet a more natively sculptural medium. Interestingly, while knitting is considered more technically difficult than crochet, knitting has long since been automated, yet there are no machines that can replicate crochet. The mechanics of the manual motions in three-dimensional space are just too complex.

Christine Wertheim

Plasticene Middens and Plastic Fossils, or the Lithospheric Imaginary

1

Fig. 1 → Detail of *Helsinki Coral Forest*, created
for the 2021 Helsinki Biennial by Christine
and Margaret Wertheim and "Team Finland"

The total mass of plastic produced since 1950 is close to six billion metric tons, "enough to bundle the entire planet in plastic wrap."[1] But, due to the lag time between collection of statistics and the accumulation of actual stuff, this figure does *not* include the staggering amount generated in the last two years due to COVID-19: estimated by researchers at 1.6 million tons per day, including the 3.4 billion single-use face masks and shields discarded daily.[2] Unfortunately, the unanticipated occurrence of a pandemic resulted in unmanageable levels of biomedical plastic wastes and reversed the momentum of a years-long global battle to reduce plastic waste pollution. And much of this stuff now circulates in *us*, as microplastics seep, via air, water, and earth, into all living cells on Earth. Now plastic fuses with flesh forming a new kind of life. However, today the most visible signs of plastic's amazing liquescence lie in the geological realm, where plastic sand and plastic fossils are now sought-after items with art-market cachet.[3]

As early as 1938, Russian scientists conceived of "scientific thought as a geological force," and even used the term "Anthropocene" to refer to a potentially emerging geological period.[4] But the new word was widely popularized in 2000 when atmospheric chemist Paul J. Crutzen declared human influence on the Earth's atmosphere so significant as to constitute a definable geological era.[5] Since then many other names for this age have been offered, starting with those proposed by people who object that not *all* human presence is registered here, or even any humans, but rather *capital*, the economic matrix in which only some, though ever-increasingly more, people are now enmeshed. Hence one alternative: Capitalocene. Other proposals include the Petrolocene, the Terrorcene, and the Chthulucene—the latter referring to the oldest gods who mostly lived underground, and still, according to some, influence life on the crust—see the uncategorizable tales of H. P. Lovecraft. But my favorite is the Plasticene, not just because it registers the ubiquitous spread of an artificial substance throughout the biosphere, but because it draws attention to the plastic-*ity* of Nature itself.

In 2006, when Margaret Wertheim and I learned of the Great Pacific Garbage Patch (GPGP), that whorl of plastic waste accumulating in the Pacific Ocean, we vowed to save all our own domestic plastic for five years. Four years later we had to admit defeat; for to save is to wash, and washing plastic, especially food-related stuff is a time-consuming business. By then we had accumulated 440 pounds. We call it *The Midden*, after the trash heaps found around ancient sites of human habitation that often provide anthropological insight. For two people over four years, 440 pounds is not so bad. We could not do it now, as the quantum of plastic packaging ever increases. For instance, our favorite containers of pickled ginger recently sprouted yet another skin of "protection" in the form of an internal hard-plastic lid, inside the outer lid, which is itself now wrapped in a layer of clear soft plastic. How many condoms do we need to protect ourselves? And from what?

1   Angus Chen, "Rocks Made of Plastic Found on Hawaiian Beach," *Science*, June 4, 2014, https://www.science mag.org/news/2014/06/rocks-made -plastic-found-hawaiian-beach (accessed October 8, 2021).

2   Nsikak U. Benson, David E. Bassey, Thavamani Palanisami, "COVID Pollution: Impact of COVID-19 Pandemic on Global Plastic Waste Footprint," *Heliyon* 7, no. 2 (February 2021), https://doi.org/10.1016/j.heliyon.2021 .e06343 (accessed October 8, 2021).

3   Kirsty Robertson, "Plastiglomerate," *flux Journal* 78 (December 2016), https://www.e-flux.com/journal/78 /82878/plastiglomerate/ (accessed October 8, 2021).

4   Meghan Ogden, "The Anthropocene" Viewed from Vernadsky's Noosphere," *LaRouchePAC* Action, https://action .larouchepac.com/_the_anthropocene.

5   "As of March 2021, neither the International Commission on Stratigraphy (ICS) nor the International Union of Geological Sciences (IUGS) has officially approved the term as a recognized subdivision of geologic time, although the Anthropocene Working Group (AWG) of the Subcommission on Quaternary Stratigraphy (SQS) of the ICS voted in April 2016 to proceed towards a formal . . . proposal to define the Anthropocene epoch in the geologic time scale . . ." See https://en.wikipedia .org/wiki/Anthropocene#cite_note-17.

Fig. 3 → Plastic debris from the Great
Pacific Garbage Patch, gathered on Kamilo
Beach, Hawaii, by Captain Charles Moore

3

And as we accumulated this stuff, we also began to crochet it: the plastic bags, videotapes, gift wrap, etc., anything that could be turned into a plastic yarn. And from these we started making a *Toxic Reef* as a postmodern synthetic sibling to the mimetic beauty of our yarn-based works, themselves evoking healthy living reefs.

In an early video piece I used the film *Eve of Destruction*, a 1991 B-movie masterpiece about a female cyborg who is also an atomic bomb. The plot concerns her growing consciousness of her destructive potential and her ultimate refusal to become what she was designed to be. At the time, I saw it as a metaphor for our plastic-ensorcelled age. *This* will kill *that;* artificial substances will kill Nature. In 2021 the distinction between natural and artificial is no longer sustainable, if ever it was, and plastic has become an emblem for a new hybrid world, precisely because of its astonishing malleability. Indeed, as Ranjan Ghosh proposes in "The Plastic Controversy," plastic has become a figural event transforming the way we think; especially about our environment, and our own entanglement with this.[6] In the *Crochet Coral Reef* project, the yarn reefs are now entangled with a growing array of plastic coral entities—in addition to the *Toxic Reef* is a grove of towering plastic *Coral Forest* sculptures and a variety of miniature plastic *Pod Worlds*, each a small imagined universe of petrochemical enchantments that rest on beds of plastic "sand" gathered from Kamilo Beach in Hawaii by Captain Charles Moore, discoverer of the Great Pacific Garbage Patch.

The überfigure of the new plasticity—one could call it the contemporary *arche-fossil*—is the object-substance known as plastiglomerate, encountered by Moore and Patricia Corcoran on islands surrounding the Garbage Patch ↗ figs. 4–7.

6 Ranjan Ghosh, "The Plastic Controversy," *Critical Enquiry* (blog), February 4, 2021, https://critinq.wordpress.com/2021/02/04/the-plastic-controversy (accessed October 8, 2021).

Fig. 4 → Plastiglomerate from Kamilo Beach, Hawaii

Fig. 5, 6 → Plastiglomerates, 2013. These found object artworks were the subject of a scientific study by geologist Patricia Corcoran, oceanographer Charles Moore, and artist Kelly Jazvac. The pieces were collected at Kamilo Beach, Hawaii. The stones (readymades) consist of a mix of molten plastic debris and beach sediment, including sand, wood, and rock.

Plastiglomerate is a modern rock-like substance formed by the melting and cooling of bits of refused plastic on terrestrial plains such as beaches, but also on deserts, roads, and playgrounds. As the plastic fluxes from solid to liquid and back again, heating and softening, cooling and congealing, it takes in matter from its surrounds—sand, dirt, bits of shell, and other detritus. The result is a compound substance, formed literally by natural processes, similar to those that create granite, yet it is partially, if not mostly, plastic ↗ fig. 3.

In the spirit of "transcendental geology," Ghosh suggests, that this bizarre, erratic substance manifests a "poesis in petrology," a new "geopoetical thought [in] the lithospheric imaginary."[7] Here, plastic, moves from being formulated for us, to finally (per)-forming *itself*.[8] Furthermore, in this new-found geo-reality, the whole of the Earth becomes manifest as an *event,* demonstrating the extraordinary plasticity of Nature.[9] That an artificial product made for pure human convenience

7 Ghosh, "Plastic Controversy."

8 Ghosh.

4

5

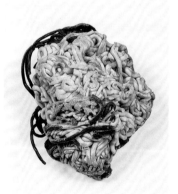

6

7

could produce this revelation (even if it has also come into view by other means) is little short of miraculous; though it may also lead to our demise. But how long will plastic actually last? Will it remain, as some propose, in the fossil record for millions of years?

Paleontologist Jan Zalasiewicz doubts it.[10] Plastic melts, and rocks in their history often pass through great depths and temperatures precisely because of those same tectonic processes by which granite is formed. These would melt the plastic beyond recognition, perhaps even destroying its molecular structure and returning it to its compound elements, mainly carbon. Thus, geologist Philip Gibbard imagines, plastics might "revert back to a source of oil from whence they came."[11] However, not all plastics behave in the same way, and the routes to plasti-fossilization are legion. It is thus possible, according to Zalasiewicz, that while the formation and stabilization of whole plastic strata is unlikely in the long term, some very fine remnants may be preserved in the same way that the memories of some leaves and bones are saved as fossilized shadows in rock. Just so, Zalasiewicz speculates, some lasting evidence of plastic may be conserved as a thin carbon film. In some rare cases, you may well be left with the shape of a flat plastic bottle ever so lightly etched on the surface of a stone.[12]

9   Ghosh.

10   Chen, "Rocks Made of Plastic Found
     on Hawaiian Beach."

11   Chen.

12   Chen.

The list below is the hard-plastic waste items generated by Christine Wertheim over a ten-week period in 2013.

In addition, there were 89 soft plastic bags and wrappers, plus 36 pieces of composite packaging: 1 plate, 3 CD holders, 6 CDs, 3 tubes, 1 plastic slate, 1 plate, 4 yoghurt cups, 3 medication bottles, 3 lids, 1 sponge, 2 large containers, 1 mid-size container, 2 lids, 4 cups, 3 plates, 4 container caps, 1 spice bottle, 1 lid, 1 sponge, 3 scoops, 1 letter R, 1 lid, 1 bottle, 1 lid, 1 cheese pot, 3 forks, 1 yoghurt pot, 4 cards, 2 highlighters, 2 pens, 2 bottles, 2 bottle tops, 2 pen lids, 1 fork, 1 knife, 1 spoon, 2 mascaras, 2 pill bottles, 2 lids, 2 crochet wrappers, 5 container caps, 6 bottles, 6 bottle tops, 9 forks, 4 can lids, 24 containers, 24 lids (party), 1 spice bottle, 3 coffee mates, 1 cup, 1 bleach bottle, 1 detergent bottle, 2 dye bottles, 2 pairs gloves, 2 tubes, 2 sachets, 1 shampoo bottle, 1 conditioner bottle, 1 packet floss, 1 floss wrapper.

We urge readers to try this exercise for themselves. Keep and list all your own plastic trash from a month, or even a week. You'll be astonished how much you use. And ask yourself this: which of these items will survive? And how long will they endure in the environment?

Fig. 8 → Detail of *Helsinki Coral Forest* crocheted from recycled plastics by three thousand Helsinki Satellite reefers. Sculpture curated by Christine and Margaret Wertheim with Lotta Kjellberg, Elina Ahlstedt, Noora El Harouny, and Tuija Maija Piironen

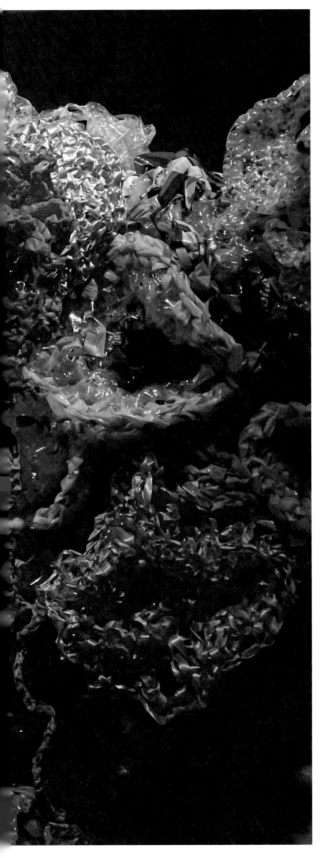

Fig. 9 → Coral growing on plastic
trash and discarded car parts in a tank
at the Monterey Bay Aquarium

9

Christine and Margaret Wertheim

Helsinki Reef Tragedy: Art Imitates Life

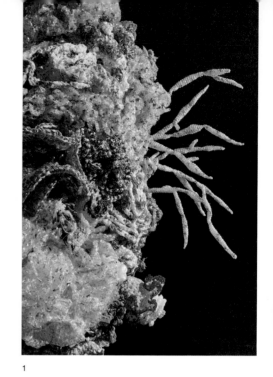

1

Remember those COVID months when we all were stockpiling toilet paper? This emblem of viral infection—a harbinger perhaps of a new era in human-microbial relations—has a resonance in the *Crochet Coral Reef* project that played out over the summer of 2021 in an uncanny smashup of parasitical invasion and global warming. At the intersection of a Venn diagram linking COVID, contagion, craft, and climate change was toilet paper—or to be more precise, plastic toilet paper *packaging*.

As ocean temperatures rise, coral reefs everywhere are being decimated, including *artificial* corals. Even *plastic* reefs, it seems, are now vulnerable to the forces of climate change.

The story begins when Margaret traveled to Helsinki in May 2021 to work with the people of Finland on a suite of plastic *Coral Forest* sculptures commissioned for the inaugural Helsinki Biennial, whose theme, "The Same Sea," resonated so well with the crochet reef project. The Biennial had also commissioned a local, community-made *Satellite Reef*, and along with the woolen corals for that installation, the three thousand participants from across Finland had crocheted a vast mass of plastic corals. Margaret's aim was to help them curate this pile into a series of plastic coralline sculptures.

In most local crochet reef projects, plastic constitutes a small fraction of the total because many people don't like the feel or look of its trashy aesthetics and it can be hard on the hands. Moreover, if one crafts with plastic bags, these have to be cut into strips before the crochet begins, which can be tedious for even committed crafters. A brilliant solution was hit upon in Finland when local reef organizer Lotta Kjellberg, approached a manufacturer of plastic packaging about possible by-products that might lend themselves to crochet. At first perplexed, the company Amerplast agreed to send a truckload of plastic strips produced in the making of toilet paper packaging.

Those large packs of loo paper we hoarded come wrapped in plastic film, and as the film comes off the production line, an inch-wide strip is cut from the edge, making it a perfect medium for crochet. Two hundred kilos of the stuff was delivered in a dumpster to Kjellberg's door, which she distributed around Helsinki in individual bags, itself a time-consuming task of devotional recycling. Dotted with dashes of printer's ink and tinted blueish-violet, this material resembles some weirdly elegant videotape, and its availability in such quantity enabled the creation of a huge number of color-coordinated plastic corals. We could not have wished for a better scenario.

The four resulting sculptures were masterful testimonies to the power of collaborative community art and to the potentiality of plastic itself. Each one was bursting

The *Helsinki Satellite Reef* was exhibited as part of the 2021 Helsinki Biennial. Nearly three thousand Finns contributed to this endeavor.

The project was hosted by the Helsinki Art Museum and overseen by HAM's Education Curator Lotta Kjellberg and Curator for Public Art Aleksandra Kiskonen. *Helsinki Biennial 2021: The Same Sea* was curated by Pirkko Siitari and Taru Tappola.

The *Helsinki Coral Forest* sculptural suite, exhibited in an underground ammunition bunker on Vallisaari island, was curated by Christine and Margaret Wertheim in conjunction with Lotta Kjellberg, Elina Ahlstedt, Noura El Harouny, and Tuija Maija Piironen, aka "Team Finland."

2

3

4

with life, each a synthetic ecology composed from hundreds of plastic pieces that rehabilitated rubbish through the lens of female craft. Together they were displayed in a nineteenth-century bunker built by the Russian army, one of a series of semiunderground structures resembling miniature orthodox cathedrals, originally used to store gunpowder and now repurposed as a location for Biennial art.

But over the summer of 2021, Finland experienced one of the hottest and wettest periods in its recorded history. Further north, the Greenland ice sheet was drenched in rain, an unheard-of phenomenon—it *never* rains in Greenland—and an ominous sign of the forces being unleashed in our atmosphere. On Vallisaari, the island where the artworks were displayed, the bunkers became infested with mold. Video screens dripped with slime, projectors burnt out; but these were solvable problems. For the corals, a more permanent tragedy ensued. Blobs of mold blossomed on the pedestals and on the understructures holding up the works. Now, instead of coming to Germany as part of the Museum Frieder Burda exhibition, these beautiful monsters have had to be destroyed, for you cannot bring mold-infested work into a gallery space.

Art has imitated life. Even *plastic* sea creatures can't withstand the onslaught of humanity's petrochemical ensorcellment.

Is there a solution? Yes. Mold can be killed by soaking infested items in alcohol or gassing them in a nitrogen chamber, a common museological practice when art gets infested with pests. If these works were by Anish Kapoor or Jeff Koons the means would likely have been found. But the *Helsinki Coral Forests* are not made by an individual validated Art World "genius." Their creators are an assortment of female citizens, effectively "folk artists" operating at a tangent to the professionalized art scene. In the history of the *Crochet Coral Reef* project almost none of the *Satellite Reefs* have been kept because community art installations, seen as *amateur* works, are rarely deemed worthy of the resources required to store and conserve them, a problem bedeviling much that falls under the rubric of "outsider art."[1] So they disappear, mimetically reflecting the fate of their living cousins, who also soon may be mere memories.

The case of the Helsinki sculptures is a particular tragedy, for they were among the most enigmatic and beautiful of the *people's* productions. "Gorgeous, absurd and socially productive, these are rare works of art," and as such they deserved a place in a permanent museum collection.[2]

1   See Doug Harvey's essay discussing the Crochet Coral Reef community projects in relation to the tradition of "folk" and "outsider" art on pages 54–61 of this catalog.

2   This quote was originally used by Pulitzer Prize–winning *Los Angeles Times* art critic Christopher Knight to describe our plastic *Coral Forest* sculptures, and we repurpose it here. Christopher Knight, "Art Review: 'The Loop Show' at Beacon Arts Building," *Los Angeles Times*, December 21, 2011, https://latimesblogs.latimes.com /culturemonster/2011/12/art-review -loop-show-beacon-arts.html (accessed October 11, 2021).

Amita Deshpande

reCharkha EcoSocial: Upcycling Plastic in India

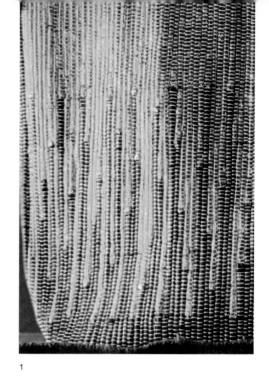

1

Plastic Waste:
An Indian Story[1]

Christine Wertheim on reCharkha

In the last seventy years, 6.3 billion metric tons of plastic waste have been generated, of which *only nine percent* has been recycled.[1] Worldwide, three hundred tons of plastic waste are spawned each year, nearly equivalent to the weight of the entire human population.[2] Every minute we collectively junk ten million plastic bags, one million plastic bottles, and many more disposables, plates, glasses, cutlery, wrappers, etc. Half the total plastic produced today is designed to be *single use only,* meaning that most will only be deployed by the consumer for a few minutes, or a few seconds, then tossed. A recent report cited by *The Guardian* newspaper stated that in the United States greenhouse gas emissions from the production of plastics will most likely outstrip those from coal-burning by 2030, releasing at least 232 metric tons of gas annually.[3] This is the world's midden. How much is yours?

Not surprisingly, plastic is everywhere—in the ground, in the water, and the air. Another report in *The Guardian* notes that microplastic particles now pervade all bodies of water on the planet except those locked at the poles in permafrost. Plastic particles are in every living organism on Earth, from grass to us. But just because this is the case does not mean we should give up. India offers a prime example of what can be achieved.[4] In the city of Pune and the nearby village of Khoripada in western India, a remarkable organization called *reCharkha* employs local tribal villagers to upcycle discarded plastics into useable items such as bags, fashion accessories, home décor, and office stationery. As with the *Toxic Reef, reCharkha's* workers create from plastic shopping bags, gift wrap, and other refused materials. Only here, the objects are woven and spun rather than crocheted. Founded by Amita Deshpande, a former IT engineer who has worked extensively in sustainable development, *reCharkha* offers local employment within a framework of environmental solutions while reawakening and revalorizing traditional handworked tools and techniques. Deshpande's dream is to develop a sustainable village and live in it herself. This is her story.

1   Laura Parker, "A Whopping 91 Percent of Plastic Isn't Recycled," National Geographic Resource Library, July 5, 2019, https://www.nationalgeographic.org/article/whopping-91-percent-plastic-isnt-recycled/ (accessed October 13, 2021).

2   "Our Planet Is Drowning in Plastic Pollution—It's Time for Change!," UNEP—UN Environment Programme, https://www.unep.org/interactive/beat-plastic-pollution/ (accessed October 13, 2021).

3   Maya Yang, "US Plastics to Outstrip Coal's Greenhouse Gas Emissions by 2030, Study Finds," *The Guardian*, October 21, 2021, https://www.theguardian.com/environment/2021/oct/21/plastics-greenhouse-gas-emissions-climate-crisis.

4   "Fact Sheet on Plastic Waste in India," teri—The Energy and Resources Institute, https://www.teriin.org/sites/default/files/files/factsheet.pdf (accessed October 13, 2021).

Fig. 2 → Suhana weaving plastic-waste
reels on a traditional handloom

3

As so many before me, the world over, I have seen in my own lifetime the arrival and pernicious spreading of the monster that is plastic. Growing up in a small Indian town in the 1980s, I never saw plastic packaging. At the grocery store everything was wrapped in old newspaper, with bulky items packed in leftover cardboard boxes, and liquids and grains put in reused cans and bottles. Even at the market we brought our own cloth bags. What waste we generated—food and paper scraps—was either tossed out for animals to eat or left to turn back into compost. Like everywhere, before the onset of modern packaging, our garbage was handled by a well-managed triad of humans, plants, and animals. Only in the 1990s did plastic bags start appearing in our part of the world, first given out free by up-market department stores, then slowly creeping into shops of every kind. But still, they were considered precious, and saved for reuse owing to their durability and capacity to hold liquids. This reuse mindset is still common in Indian people of older generations. But then came the disposables, as "convenience" and "time-saving" became key marketing terms, especially for products aimed at women, who still do most of the activities involving cleaning, from dishes to diapers.[5] Disposable bags, disposable cutlery, disposable cups, disposable straws, everything! And so the Plastic Age began.

In eighth grade I won an interschool competition for my presentation on solid waste. But the prize was secondary to what I discovered about the problem and its solutions: refuse, reuse, repurpose, recycle. Understanding then where we were headed, I vowed to cut my own plastic consumption and try influencing others to do the same. Twenty years later, I head an organization upscaling waste plastic into new wares and raising awareness of sustainable practices.

Though Indian streets are awash in refuse, at sixty percent, the country's overall plastic recycling rate is among the world's highest.[6] Most of this happens in the unorganized sector and is very labor intensive. But with India's population being its ultimate resource, recycling creates a great deal of much-needed employment. Indeed, there are many Indian organizations recycling and upcycling plastic.[7] As everywhere, the biggest impediment to more successful recycling in our country

5   For an excellent account of how "convenience" and single-use plastic containers were pushed onto consumers, see Heather Rodgers, "A Brief History of Plastic," *Brooklyn Rail*, May 2005, http://www.brooklynrail.org /2005/05/express/a-brief-history-of -plastic (accessed October 13, 2021).

6   "Fact Sheet on Plastic Waste in India," teri—The Energy and Resources Institute, https://www.teriin.org/sites /default/files/files/factsheet.pdf (accessed October 13, 2021).

7   Kamala Thiagarajan, "The Man Who Paves India's Roads with Old Plastic," *The Guardian*, July 9, 2018, https: //www.theguardian.com/world/2018 /jul/09/the-man-who-paves-indias -roads-with-old-plastic.

Fig. 4 → Asha and Vandana sort plastic waste
for making upcycled, handwoven products
such as the *Jhola Tote* in this image

4

is the problem of separation—sorting waste into its many different categories so it can be processed, recycled, or disposed of more effectively. In Japan whole villages and cities have mandatory waste segregation where every household has to sort their trash into different categories, sometimes as many as forty-five, before depositing it as local recycling centers.[8] Government's role here is key, and now we have the beginning of this with the Extended Producer Responsibility Act of India.[9]

At reCharkha we don't simply recycle, we *upcycle*. We don't just turn used plastic into a cleaner plastic for remanufacture into newer products; we directly make products *from* waste, thereby leaping over a huge unnecessary step in wasteful recycling. Pronounced "Re-Char-K-ha," the name is a compound of the English prefix *re*, meaning "again," "afresh," or "anew," originally from Latin, and *charkha*, a Persian word for "spinning wheel," with origins in Sanskrit. During India's fight for liberation, the charkha became a symbol of *Swadesi* or independence, when spinning one's own yarn and weaving one's own fabric literalized the Indian sense of self-reliance and autonomy from British industrialists who had for centuries dominated our textile industry, subjugating our people in the process.

8   There are many videos on Youtube.

9   Ministry of Environment, Forest and Climate Change, "Guideline Document: Uniform Framework for Extended Producers Responsibility Under Plastic Waste Management Rules," June 2020, http://moef.gov.in/wp-content/uploads /2020/06/Final-Uniform-Framework -on-EPR-June2020-for-comments.pdf (accessed October 13, 2021).

"We cannot do this merely as individuals, it also has to be done collectively in tandem with governments and other bodies with political and economic power, as common citizens of our planet."

Most people we employ are local tribal members, many of whom must end school early to support their families and leave their villages to work in larger cities far away. reCharkha offers them employment within the context of their own communities. Take Jitesh Bhanwar, one of our lead-weavers; he's a local tribal youth, belonging to the Warli tribe. Mute and deaf by birth, Jitesh grew up in the village where there are no special schools for his educational needs; at reCharkha he has been trained in a highly technical traditional craft at which he now excels. Vandana Vartha, also from the Warli tribe, completed her tenth grade schooling and had mostly stayed home helping her mother until reCharkha arrived in her village. After starting as an assistant artisan, she now works as a technical supervisor overseeing a group of people and coordinating various lines of production.

Most importantly, we use a great deal of the difficult-to-recycle material found in multilayered packets, or MLPs—roughly thirty thousand pieces per month. We also employ traditional Indian techniques of spinning and weaving using humble hands and feet rather than modern automated machines. First, local tribal women wash and sanitize the plastic and sort it by color. Next, they cut it manually with scissors to produce long fibers. These fibers are then woven one by one on a handloom, so that each piece is unique. By this means, reCharkha provides over seven hundred days of livelihood for tribal women and artisans every month, and over one hundred days of livelihood for waste pickers.

However, recycled products are not a long-term alternative to the problem of disposable plastic, either for India or the world. The final solution is not only upcycling and recycling, but the four R's that precede these: Refuse, Reduce, Reuse, Repair. This is something we all need to think about in the context of our lives wherever we live. In India we are approaching one and a half billion people, and the world totality is approaching seven and a half billion. That's a lot of people generating a lot of plastic waste. We cannot do this merely as individuals, it also has to be done collectively in tandem with governments and other bodies with political and economic power, as common citizens of our planet.

Cord Riechelmann

Ernst Haeckel, the Biologist and Artist

1

The *Crochet Coral Reef* project confronts viewers with the complex issue of the difference between individual and collective organisms, and individual and collective construction of artworks. Is a given crochet reef—say, the installation at Museum Frieder Burda—a single work? Or is it rather a collection of many individual works coming together to form a larger unity or aesthetic organism? This question was also central to the great and controversial nineteenth-century biologist Ernst Haeckel, whose drawings of sea creatures remarkably echo some traditional crochet doilies.

The inclusion of Haeckel's drawing of siphonophores in the exhibition of the *Crochet Coral Reef* in Baden-Baden directly confronts viewers with this issue as well as with Haeckel's problematic work and career. In addition to the Latin name, the caption of his illustration bears the German term *Staatsquallen*, or "federal jellyfish," demonstrating Haeckel's tendency to relate natural phenomena to the political realm of human history ↗ fig. 2. It also reflects his attempt to articulate two irreconcilable stances in an ongoing debate about siphonophores in the second half of the nineteenth century involving two of the most famous biologists of the era: British scientist Thomas Henry Huxley, also known as "Darwin's bulldog," and American scientist Louis Agassiz, a professor at Harvard.

At the heart of the debate was the question of whether siphonophores are composed of individuals in colonies or whether they are actually individual organisms whose parts function as specialized organs.[1] Haeckel's attempt at reconciliation was his proposition to use the descriptive term "federal." For him, they were both: colonies that are composed of many individuals and active "individuals" that, similar to a state, functioned as a unit, unifying many individuals into a whole. While the debate about the status of siphonophores is still unresolved, there are many indications that both theories—the "polyperson" theory and the "polyorgan" theory—are correct in their premises. For this reason, siphonophores remain one of the unsolved paradoxes of biology to this day.

Due to points that can only be touched upon here, Haeckel is one of the most controversial and enigmatic biologists of the modern era. The man himself is admittedly another paradox: although he detested all forms of disease, he chose to study medicine. He then became one of the most passionate advocates of evolution theory following the publication of Charles Darwin's *On the Origin of Species* in German in 1860 ↗ fig. 5, while hardly developing or changing his own worldview in the course of his life. His books, which had a great impact on socialist thinkers such as Leon Trotsky, Mao Zedong, and Walter Ulbricht, deny the mentally ill the right to live. They provide detailed instructions on euthanasia "using a dose of morphine or cyanide." After his death, these instructions were to be implemented by others. He is an excellent example of the danger of removing limits from scientific activity and allowing the results to be used as a basis for formulating ideological

1 A similar issue pertains to the *Crochet Coral Reef* project, where a question arises as to whether individual makers are a collection of *associating* artists, or whether they are one vast artistic "entity."

Fig. 2 → Ernst Haeckel, "Porpema. Siphonophorae.—Staatsquallen," lithograph,
13 ⁵⁄₈ × 10 ¹⁄₄ in. / 34.6 × 26 cm in *Kunstformen der Natur* (Art Forms in Nature),
Verlag des Bibliographischen Instituts, Leipzig and Vienna, 1904, plate 17

3

convictions. It would, however, be similarly wrong to dismiss Haeckel as the social Darwinist, racist, and nationalist that he was and to stop investigating his work. Indignation is both unhelpful and explains nothing. The influence of his most popular works was significant, and their influence is still felt: *Die Welträtsel* (1899) ↗ fig. 4, published in English as *The Riddle of the Universe* in 1901, and *Kunstformen der Natur* ↗ fig. 1, which was issued between 1899 and 1904 as a series of booklets and published in English as *Art Forms in Nature* in 1974. The latter consists of one hundred color lithographs of plants and animals that are intended to demonstrate one thing in their eccentric arrangement: the perfect symmetrical beauty of natural forms. For Haeckel, symmetry provided a principle of design that linked one-celled radiolarians living in marine plankton, with their rich, bizarrely shaped skeletons, and animals such as hummingbirds and antelopes.

Two eras are superimposed in the prints. Still based on Goethe's concept of intuitive thought and the related confusion of natural philosophy in the Romantic period, they also reflect the visual sensations with which the world's fairs of the late nineteenth century and early twentieth centuries captivated and hypnotized their visitors. German writer Durs Grünbein has demonstrated in his essay "Das grandiose Buch" (The Grandiose Book) how Haeckel's handling of objects in his drawings was influenced by contemporary art of his time and how, in turn, Haeckel's work inspired contemporary architects, painters, fashion designers, and authors. It has also been an influence on a variety of makers in the *Crochet Coral Reef* project, some of whom have taken his elegant, tendriled illustrations as inspirations for crafting fantastical sea forms.[2]

4

2   Foremost among crochet coral "reefers" who have emulated Haeckel is Dallas, Texas, contributor Evelyn Hardin, who crocheted a series of finely wrought jellyfish from embroidery floss, based on his drawings.

5

In line with the dominant style of Art Nouveau, which can now be studied in the Paris metro, Haeckel's work also influenced Jugendstil and Art Deco. For Grünbein, Haeckel's natural art forms are also aesthetically compatible with the computer-generated Mandelbrot sets of modern chaos theory. For viewers who are accustomed to computer simulations, it is, in fact, quite hard to resist the psychedelic effect of Haeckel's images, and it is often difficult to ascertain if the forms are real or figments of fantasy.

Haeckel was long undecided about whether he should be a landscape painter or a scientist. Inspired by travel literature and Lorenz Oken's monumental *Allgemeine Naturgeschichte für alle Stände* (A General History of Nature for All Classes, 1834–41) when he was young, Haeckel wanted to be an explorer. A drawing that he made when he was sixteen, entitled *Nationalversammlung der Vögel* (National Assembly of Birds), indicates that even as an adolescent he was unable to conceive of nature outside of social movements.

When Haeckel enrolled at university in Berlin in 1852, he was confronted with the problem that biology was not an independent subject, so he registered for medicine. Although he received a doctorate in medicine and was certified as a general practitioner, he never actually practiced medicine. Instead, he did research on radiolarians and discovered 144 new species of radiolarians in the Strait of Messina on a study trip to Italy. While Haeckel was working on his first major publication, a study on radiolarians entitled *Monographie der Radiolaren*, which was printed in 1862, Darwin's *On the Origin of Species* was released. For anyone endeavoring to establish a discipline as independent within an institution, it is helpful to link one's results to a general theory that is not yet represented in another department, and Darwin's evolution theory offered Haeckel the optimal prerequisites for such a step. The speed with which Haeckel integrated Darwin's concepts in his own theory paid off, and in 1865 the first proper professorship for zoology was established in Jena for Haeckel. The independence of the discipline, now that zoology was emancipated from medicine, opened the door for experimental biological research to be established in the fields of botany, zoology, and physiology.

Haeckel's part in this development in university history was considerable. Even after becoming a professor, he continued his own experimental work with simple marine life forms. He published monographs on trunked jellyfish (*Medusa geryonida*), calcareous sponges, medusas, and siphonophore, all of which were pioneering studies in their fields. These books established his reputation as an excellent marine zoologist and resulted in an invitation to participate in the evaluation of the catches from the most famous oceanographic expedition of the era on the HMS *Challenger* between 1873 and 1876. Haeckel contributed 230 plates and descriptions of 3,702 new species to the fifty-volume report of the findings. While his work as a taxonomist and practicing morphologist is uncontested to this day, it is difficult to accept when he attempts to formulate general laws. The most prominent example of this is his most famous formula, known as the Biogenetic Law or the Recapitulation Theory. According to this theory, ontogeny (the development of individual organisms) recapitulates phylogeny (the evolutionary history of organisms). As stimulating as the theory was for research, it was also contested from the very beginning. Even though the law has since been refuted, the questions that it posed were correct. Although reconstructing the origin of organisms entails finding similarities between related forms, organisms that are not related to each other often bear a strong resemblance to each other while those that are related to each other can be utterly dissimilar. The first type of development is called analog, and the second is homologous.

Analogies can be misleading and must be ignored when investigating genealogy; only homologous designations can be used to establish interrelationships. The homologies themselves were the focus of Haeckel's research. He wanted to prove that different animals in their embryonic stages of development were so similar that in the past eras they were united in common ancestors. The fact that he not infrequently used the same picture in his lectures on the embryonic stages of different animals led to a scientific scandal in the 1870s, though it optimally reflected Haeckel's intentions. Nevertheless, the difference between analogies and homologies still applies. Only in this point does the problem of Haeckel's overall approach become apparent.

All of Haeckel's social concepts, which are derived from natural empiricism, are obviously nothing other than analogies, both in terms of language and images. This brings us back to the plates of the natural forms and siphonophores. Siphonophores are related to corals and jellyfish, and in the words of Stephen Jay Gould, they are "a most ingenious paradox." Even today, it is still not known how to determine if they are individual organisms or colonies, which is why they

"... just as it is an open question as to the exact nature of the relationship between individual crochet coral pieces and the vast woolen ecology of a completed museum installation. Like siphonophores and living corals, crochet reefs and their makers confound traditional categorical distinctions."

continue to be called *Staatsquallen* in German, using the word for "federal," while their individual parts are still referred to as "individuals," although the terms are usually set in quotation marks to indicate their metaphoric use. Haeckel, however, was less cautious. His aesthetically pleasing drawings lack precision in biological terms due to his exaggeration of their symmetry. He also compared their complex colonies with "more highly developed" human social forms, in contrast to the simple colonies of other cnidarians, which were considered to be related to the lifestyles of "primitive" humans with limited division of labor.[3] He frequently uses such analogies in his works, such as when he played the "thinking soul of civilized humans" against the "souls of animals that are devoid of thought." Ultimately, in spite all of his anticlerical revolutionary attitudes, his stance was caught in the conventional classic view of humans as the highest event of creation in his view of nature.

Yet despite Haeckel's problematic, not to say racist social theories, his drawings of sea creatures have had widespread effects within the realms of art and design, making him an important figure for cultural reference and reflection. The entire movement of Art Nouveau owes at least something to his inspiration. A pavilion at the 1900 world's fair in Paris was designed after one of his radiolarian drawings, and since then countless artists and designers have been inspired by his visions from the sea. Most important for the *Crochet Coral Reef* project is Haeckel's interest in the question of whether some seagoing life forms such as siphonophores are composed of collections of individuals or whether they may possibly be a more complex and surprising mode of life in which individual organisms act as the specialized parts of a larger entity. This uncertainty surrounds *crochet* reefs too, for it is an open question in this art practice where the work of one individual maker ends and that of another begins; just as it is an open question as to the exact nature of the relationship between individual crochet coral pieces and the vast woolen ecology of a completed museum installation. Like siphonophores and living corals, crochet reefs and their makers confound traditional categorical distinctions.

3   Corals are also from the cnidarian family and are taxonomic cousins of siphonophores.

Fig. 6 → Ernst Haeckel, "Periphylla. Peromedusae.—Taschenquallen," lithograph, 13 5/8 × 10 1/4 in. / 34.6 × 26 cm, in *Kunstformen der Natur* (Art Forms in Nature), Verlag des Bibliographischen Instituts, Leipzig and Vienna, 1904, plate 38

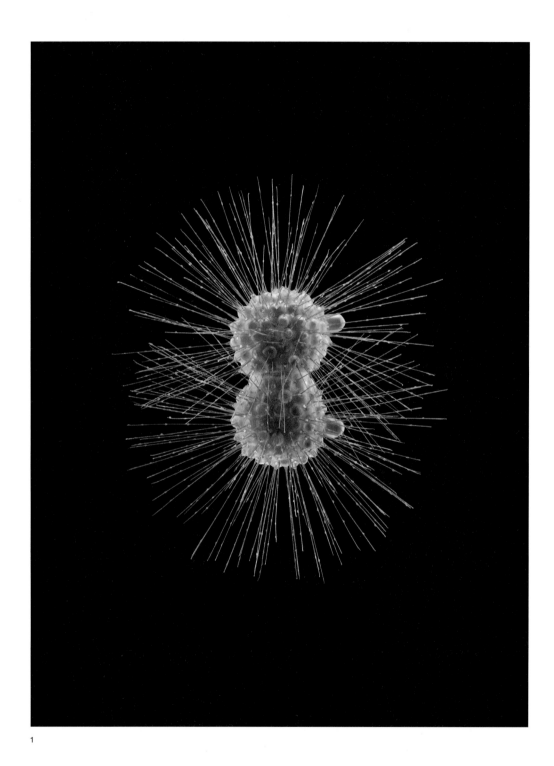

Blaschka Models

Christine Wertheim

For centuries, at least in Europe, there has been a desire for long-lasting representations of difficult-to-see natural phenomena, such as the interiors of the reproductive organs of flowers. Whole crafts grew up around this need. In the seventeenth century, for instance, crafters turned botanical and anatomical drawings into three-dimensional models made from papier-mâché: flowers, insects, human organs, and many other creaturely items were emulated. Thousands of these surreal objects languish in the basements of almost every European natural history museum.

In line with this trend, two glassblowers in the late nineteenth century saw a market opportunity and developed an entire line of sea creatures, from jellyfish to corals, made from individually blown glass parts stitched together with the finest of wires ↗ figs. 1–3. The father and son team of Leopold and Rudolf Blaschka even produced catalogs so museums could more easily order the marine organisms they desired.

The great and controversial biologist Ernst Haeckel, who traveled to the Mariana Trench and returned with thousands of radiolarians, microscopic organisms who make elaborate exoskeletons from silica, also produced a vast array of drawings of sea creatures, which were printed in beautiful, full-color books for the inquiring public.

The *Crochet Coral Reef* project continues this tradition of bringing beautiful renderings of hard-to-access natural phenomena to the public gaze. Here however, the works are created in crafts gendered as feminine—specifically, crochet and beading. And, like the Blaschckas and those passionate seventeenth-century papier-mâchéists, the makers of the *Crochet Coral Reef* are not generally professional scientists, but rather crafters: crafters with curiosity, ingenuity, and a desire to apply their skills to the realm of scientific pedagogy. In this sense, *Crochet Coral Reefs* are at once art and a continuation of a long history of technical scientific rendering.

Fig. 3 → Leopold and Rudolf Blaschka, Rhizostoma pulmo II, photographed by Guido Mocafico at the University Zoological Department, Vienna, 2014

Museum Frieder Burda

The Exhibition

Pages 120–21: *Baden-Baden Satellite Reef— Baden-Baden Coral Frieze* and *Coral Forest—Little Orange Follower*

Baden-Baden Satellite Reef—Baden-Baden Coral Frieze with Coral Forest—Stheno, Nin Imma, Little Orange Follower, Next Generation, and hanging wall piece *Carnation Mound*

Coral Forest—Next Generation, Stheno, and Medusa

Coral Forest—Stheno and *Medusa*, with
Baden-Baden Coral Frieze in the background

Coral Forest—Next Generation, Nin Imma, and
Little Orange Follower, with *Branched Anemone Garden*
and *Evelyn Hardin and Friends* in the background

→ *Detail of Coral Forest—Nin Imma,*
with *Baden-Baden Coral Frieze* in the
background

Pages 128–29:
Branched Anemone Garden

Pages 130–31: *Evelyn Hardin and Friends*
and *Branched Anemone Garden*   →

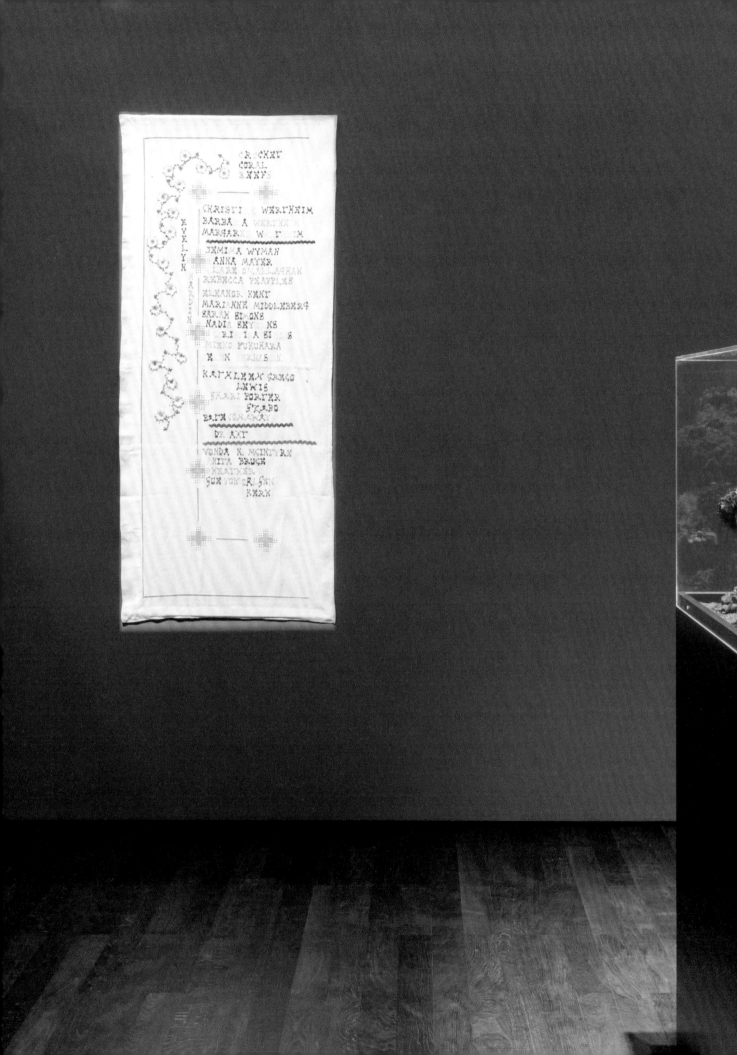

Top: *Pod Worlds—Red and White, Beaded Baroque II, Wire and Beaded,* with *Mathematics Blackboard* in the background

Bottom: *Hyperbolic Sea Snake* and *Holy Documents*

→ *Pod Worlds—Eye Jellies, Plastic Fantastic Too, Hyperbolic, Cambrian Explosion, Plastic Fantastic,* and *Pod Worlds—Red and White, Beaded Baroque II, Wire and Beaded, Beaded Baroque,* and *Wire and Beaded II*

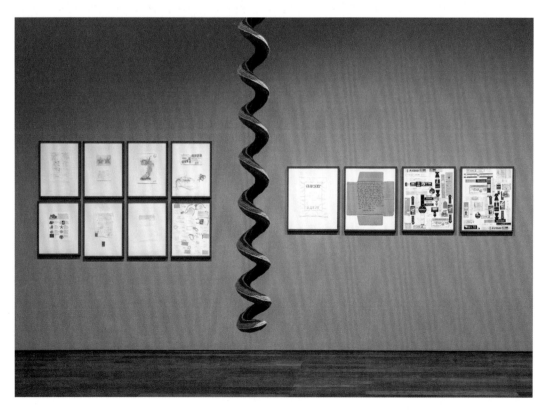

ALLES ORGANISCHE IST AUS SCHLEIM HERVORGEGANGEN,
(UND) DIE LIEBE IST AUS DEM MEERSCHAUM ENTSPRUNGEN.

Everything has been created out of sea mucous,
(and) love arises from the foam.

Lorenz Oken, 1810

Pod Worlds—Cambrian Explosion, Hyperbolic, Plastic Fantastic Too, Eye Jellies, with *Hyperbolic Sea Snake* and *Coral Forest* in the background

ALLES ORGANISCHE IST AUS SCHLEIM H
(UND) DIE LIEBE IST AUS DEM MEERSCHA

Pages 136–37: *Pod Worlds—Red and White, Beaded Baroque II, Wire and
Beaded, Beaded Baroque, Wire and Beaded II,* and *Pod Worlds—Eye Jellies,
Plastic Fantastic Too, Hyperbolic, Cambrian Explosion, Plastic Fantastic*

WE BECOME AWARE HOW MUCH FURTHER REA[SON]
SOMETIMES GO THAN IMAGINATION MAY DARE

Uns wird bewusst, wie viel weiter die Vernunft manch[mal]
als die Vorstellu[ng]

Pod Worlds—EL Wire, Staghorn Garden

Red Nudibranch Reef

← Historical documents, including doilies, books, magazines, and facsimiles of drawings by Ernst Haeckel

Glass models by Leopold and Rudolph Blaschka, and original monographs and watercolors by Ernst Haeckel

Baden-Baden Satellite Reef,
2021–2022

Baden-Baden Satellite Reef: the coral island *Variegated*

← *Baden-Baden Satellite Reef:*
detail of the coral island *Variegated*

Baden-Baden Satellite Reef:
detail of the coral island *Spotted*

Top: *Baden-Baden Satellite Reef*:
detail of the coral island *Spotted*

Bottom: *Baden-Baden Satellite Reef*:
the coral island *Neon*

→ *Baden-Baden Satellite Reef*:
detail of the coral island *Neon*

Baden-Baden Satellite Reef:
details of the coral island *Deep*

Baden-Baden Satellite Reef: the coral island *Toxic*, with the wall text listing the names of the four thousand contributors in the background

Pages 162–63: *Baden-Baden Satellite Reef*: → detail of the coral island *Tricolor*

Making Of

The team of the *Baden-Baden Satellite Reef* (from left to right):
Silke Habich, Martina Schulz, Susan Reiss, Christina Humpert,
Kathrin Dorfner, and Charlotte Reiter

Baden-Baden Satellite Reef,
2021–2022

Core Team

Reef Coordinator: Kathrin Dorfer

Curatorial Team: Christina Humpert, Martina Schulz, Charlotte Reiter, Susan Reiss, Silke Habich

List of Contributors

A

Julia Abele
Marlene Abert
Mohammad Abo Nokta
Elke Achtelik
Heike Ackermann
Maria Ackermann
Petra Ackermann
Annelore Adam
Gerlind Adam
Hildegard Adam
Sarah Ann Adam
Bettina Efigenia Adelt
Daphne Adler
Marciyeh Ahmadi
Katrin Ahrens
Elke Aidam
Milla Ainetter
Saranda Ajeti
Ghufran Al Ghaib
Laveen Al Hussein
Nele Albers
Anna Albert
Laura Alessi
Irina Alexandrovski
Cornelia Alffermann
Alfred-Welker-
  Berufsschule
Marah Alghannam
Ali
Lioba Alicke
Alisa
Elisabeth Alken
Anneke Allmer
Mohammad Almajali
Maya Almohammad
Aloys-Schreiber-Schule
  Bühl

Omar Alrashid
Lelia Alt
Helene Altenbuchner
Iris Altenhof
Sigrid Alter
Sonja Altmann-Magner
Rosalinde Amann
Amelie
Kathrin Amend
Susanne Ammann
Claudia Ammerer
Anastasija
Stefani Andernach
Sabine Andreadis
Dagmar Andres
Susanne Andres
Margarete Andresen-
  Winker
Beate Angeloni Baldoni
Tatjana Angelovska
Uschi Ankelin
Renate Ankelmann
Ann-Cathrin
Rebecca Annen
Annerose
Ellen Anschütz-Giese
Claudia Antinori
Semen Antipov
Martyna Antoniewicz
Susi Antony-Sopic
Cornelia Appel
Zeynep Arat
Claudia Arend
Alexandra Arenz
Karin Aretz
Martina Armbruster
Miriam Armbruster
Monika Armbruster
Nadja Arnold

Sibylla-Maria Arnold
Nathalie Arnolds
Gioia Arouch
Aysun Arslan
Juliane Eva
  Aschenbrenner
Katharina Aschenbrenner
ASS – Gemeinschafts-
  schule Bühl
Sonja Asser
Zenaida des Aubris
Timo Auer
Elke Aurand
Ute Aurand
Mirella Avantaggiato
Vanessa Chiara Avellina
AWO Maximiliansau
Elisabeth Azem

B

Uta Backmann
Finn Bade
Bärbel Bader
Birgit Bader
Lotte Bader
Béatrice Bader Sollberger
Iris Bader-Kühnle
Sybille Bähr
Philipp Baier
Birgit Baisch
Doris Bakenhus
Almut Bakowski-Dziobek
Elaine Balatka
Karin Balster
Beate Balzer
Isabella Bamberg
Silvia Bangert
Majid Bantla
Sandra Bantle

Ingrid Bär
Slinderela Barakat
Gabriela Barbosa Freihne
Celine Maria Barea-Reyes
Gisa Barner-Heiduck
Madeleine Barois
Michaela Baron
Ursula Baron
Justus Bartel
Isolde Barth
Maria Barth
Karin Bartoleit-Breuer
Barbara Bartzsch
Barbara Barwisch
Birgit Basedow
Angela Bassemir
Melanie Bastian
Mia Bastian
Sabine Bastiani
Felicitas Batsch
Jurate Batura Lemke
Anette Bauch
Birgit Bauer
Gina Marie Bauer
Imme-Bianca Bauer
Margarethe Bauer
Monika Bauer
Renate Bauer
Ulrike Bauer
Heike Bauer-Geils
Jutta Bauer-Seibt
Elvira Baumann
Lilian Baumann
Manuela Baumann
Nico Baumann
Heidi Baumann-Wyss
Sabine Bäumek
Uschi Baumgarten
Veronika Baumgarten

Anna Susanne
  Baumgärtner
Claudia Baumgärtner
Gabi Baumgärtner
Stefanie Baumgärtner
Renate Baumstark
Sigrid Baust
Eileen Bay
Claudia Bayer
Et Bayer
Renate Bayha
Selin Bayrak
Milena Beaujean
Fey Bechler
Clara Bechmann
Erika Beck
Margarete Beck
Stefanie Beck
Annalena Becker
Barbara Becker
Benita Becker
Françoise Becker
Hildegard Becker
Linda Becker
Monika Becker
Ulla Becker
Ursula Becker
Anna Beckmann
Claudia Beckmann
Jana Beckmann
Madita Beckmann
Monika Beckmeier-Vedder
Diana Beermann
Sabine Beers
Anna-Lisa Beese
Ursula Beforth
Gertrud Beha
Renate Beha
Eva Behr

Sabine Behr
Christina Behrens
Eva Behrens
Dorothee Behrens-Hock
Birgit Behrens-Otto
Alena Behuncikova
Susanne Beideck
Helena Beifuß
Eveline Beiter-Waldrab
Gabriele Beitmann
Cornelia Beitmüller
Emma Beitmüller
Marion Bekker
Alexandra Belendier
Gisela Bellebaum
Annette Bellendorf
Claudia Alexandra Beltz
Lilly Bemetz-Nölter
Barbara Bender
Christine Bender
Cindy Bender
Gabriele Bender-Heuchert
Kristin Benecken
Rita Benfer
Sylvia Benk
Janine Benndorf
Claudia Benthaus-Reiß
Katharina Benz
Margrit Benz
Sabine Benz
Margot Benzing
Andrea Berg
Alexandra Berger
Monika Berger
Ulrike Berger
Alexa Bergmann
Irmgard Bergmann
Judith-Maria Bergmann
Luis Bergmann

Caroline Bergner
Evelyn Bergstresser
Lisa Berhalter
Marlene Berner
Tina Bernhagen
Andrea Bernhardt
Anke Bernhardt-Flick
Bianca Bertholdt
Beatrice Bertsch
Sara Bertschi Schlegel
Karin Bestenlehner
Dagmar Bethke
Franziska Bethke
Tessa Bethke
Roberta Bettini
Gabriele Betz
Monika Betz
Thomas Betz
Christine Beuscher
Marie-Florence Beuscher
Matilda Bey
Gabriele Beyer
Lydia Beyer
Ina Bezner
Regina Bicher
Eva Bichler
Jutta Bieber
Gisela Biederbick
Elisabeth Biedermann
Brigitte Bieger
Liv Bielefeldt
Christel Biener-Strauß
Angelina Atessa Bienhüls
Biesemann
Ingeborg Bihr
Julia Bilgenroth
Christl Bilger
Julia Bilke
Martina Billinger
Katja Binder
Katrin Binder
Sabine Binder
Anna Maria Bindl
Sven Bindseil
Monika Binninger
Ingrid Birkhold
Gergö Biró
Marisa Birzle
Katrin Bischof
Ada Bischoff
Alexandra Maria Bischoff
Gertraud Bissinger
Slawka Blagojević
Elke Blanck
Lena Blanke
Gudrun Blankenburg
Celina Blasius
Susanne Blechner
Ute Blechschmidt
Elvira Bleher
Heide Bloch
Julia Bloch
Linda Bloch
Sarah Bloch
Viktoria Block
Ulla Blohberger
Doris Blum
Gunther Blum
Stefanie Blum
Susan Blumhofer
Claudia Blümle
Luise Bogie
Daniela Bogumil
Edith Bohl
Sabine Bohland
Gabi Bohle
Birgit Bohl-Ehmer
Franziska Böhler
Margit Böhler
Anke Böhm
Antonia Böhm
Isolde Böhm
Lea Böhm
Ute Böhm
Roswitha Bohmann
Jan Böhmer
Lisa Böhmer
Britta Bohn

Suse Bohn
Anna-Isabel Böhn-Bertram
Laura-Faye Bohnes
Stefanie Böhnke
Angelika Bohrer
Christiane Bohrer
Jutta Bohrmann
Ute Eva Bolick
Gudrun Boll
Claudia Bölling
Gordana Böllingèr
Elisabeth Bonneau
Sylvia Bonnin
Viwvareeya Boongeb
Gabriele Bopp
Angelika Boratynska
Claudia Borchert
Nicoletta Borelli
Manuela Borger
Monika Agnes Lena
 Borger
Anouk Bormann
Bärbel Born
Christa Bornadel
Stephanie Börner
Ellen Bosak
Elsbeth Boschert
Monika Boschert
Frau Bossette
Annette Boßle
Angela Böttcher
Catrin Böttcher
Irmela Böttger
Karima Bouazza
Monika Bouley
Katrin Boy
Elvira Bozkaya
Inci Bozkaya
Sena Bozoglu
Doris Braband-Wenz
Brigitta Brachem
Carla Bracht
Carolin Bracht
Stephanie Brand
Uta Brandecker
Hildegund Brandenburg
Katharina Brandes
Annett Brandt
Isabel Bräuer
Benjamin Braun
Carina Braun
Cornelia Braun
Jennifer Braun
Stefanie Braun
Julia Bräutigam
Lena Bräutigam
Clara Braxmaier
Nicole Braxmaier
Heike Brecht
Silvia Brede
Ursula Bree
Elina Bremer
Lonny Brendel
Martina Brendel
Petra Brendiek
Heidi Brennenstuhl
Cornelia Breuer
Chris de Breun
Christa Breuning
Ingrid Brindöpke
Stefanie Bringmann
Christine Brinks
Marie Briske
Gulchin Bro
Carolin Brockmann
Gabriele Brodersen-
 Mayer
Maria Brohl
Janina Bromann
Edda Brossmer
Petra Brückel
Madlen Brucker
Marianne Bruder
Bruderhaus Diakonie Bad
 Uracher Werkstätten,
 Arbeitsgruppe BU 05
Bruderhaus Diakonie
 Werkstätten Reutlingen

Bruderhaus Diakonie,
 Stiftung Gustav Werner
 und Haus am Berg
Barbara Brühne
Angelo de Bruijn
Valentino de Bruijn
Stefanie Brunner
Yvonne Brunner
Marliese Brunold
Silvia Brunold
Lea Bruns
Rebecca Bruskowski
Astrid Brust
Jutta Buchecker
Anne Bücheler
Lisa Bücher
Petra Buchholz
Petra Buchonnet
Sabine Buck
Anita Bühler
Gabriele Bühler
Margarete Bühler
Margaretha Bühler
Marlene Bühler
Steffi Bühler
Katrin Bührer
Ella Burchardt
Carmen Burger
Emilia Burger
Ingrid Burger
Eva Bürger
Sophie Bürger
Ingrid Bürger
Bürgergemeinschaft
 Hofheim
Fynn Burghardt
Christine Burg-Seibel
Alexander Burhof
Michaela Bürk
Sandie Burke-Späth
Anna Maria Busch
Hannelore Busch
Annelie Bütterwegge
Anita Buzengeiger-
 Mahncke

C

Claudia C.
Melanie Cammann
Elea Canders
Heike Capelle
Cornelia Capito
Silke Cappell
Carina
Caritas Tagespflege
 Albbruck
Caritasverband Kempten-
 Oberallgäu
Denise Carlini-Esser
Michelle Carnell
Claudia Geia Cartellieri
Elke Caspari
Wilfried Caspari
Cecilien-Grundschule
 Berlin
Elanur Celik
Beate Ceranski
Aranka Ceri
Rosemarie Černý
Barbara Ceskutti
Sandra Ceskutti
Frances Chang
Marianne Chang
Charlotte
Aaron Chheena
Marianne Chitralla
Gabriela Christ
Linn Sophie Christensen
Christian-Rohlfs-Realschule
 Soest
Renate Chudziak
Ronja Chur
Susanne Cifer
Carmen Cioclei
Cistercienserinnen der
 Abtei Lichtenthal
CJD Braunschweig
Clara

Hedwig Clausmeyer
Regina Clotten
Martina Coblenz
Miriam Coerdt
Blandina von Collande
Hannah Colli
Julie Comparini
Heidi Comploj
Gabriele Conigliaro
Anna Connor
Helga Conrad
Karin Coordes
Annemarie Cornelius
Hilde Corsten
Marion Craiss
Pénélope Crochetet
Monika Crocker
Agathe Croon
Eva Croon
Jürgen Croon
Lars-Magnus Croon
Edith Czuberny

D

Lucas Da Costa Rodrigues
Elisabeth Daleiden
Patricia Daly
Damian
Sonja Dammeyer
Birgit Danhamer
Monique Daniels
Gerda Danischewski
Monika Dannwolf
Karin Dantes
Ildiko Havva Dargen
Ellen Darlison
Lorena Dattilo
Karin Dauheim
Bianca Daumann
Eliza Dawid
Aysche Dawood
Andrea Daxberger
Saliwipa Meilin Deema
Heidi Degenhardt
Julia Degenhardt
Petra Degott
Annika Dehmer
Helga M. Deißler
Kirsten Deist
Aras Deligöz
Katharina Della Chiesa
Ezgi-Sila Demirhiran
Brigitte Demmel
Esther Maria Demmel
Sophia Anna-Lena Demski
Anja Dengel
Susanne Denzel
Elisabeth Deppe
Kreszentia Deppe
Umutcan Derin
Orhon Detzer
Deutsch-Amerikanischer &
 Internationaler Frauenclub
 Kaiserslautern
Beate Diallo
Barbara Dibowski
Monika Dicke
Gila Dickert
Ingrid Didra
Die Brücke für den
 Dialog e.V.
Die Strickladies aus
 Rottenburg
Emma Dieckmann
Erna Dieckmann
Christel Diehlmann
Angela Diers
Thomas Dieterle
Brigitte Dietrich
Renate Dietz
Sabine Dietz
Lisa Dietz-Schilbach
Andrea Dilger
Lena Dilger
Cornelia Dinger
Ingrid Dir
Justin Dittmann
Hella Dittrich

Birgitta Dobbertin
Evelyn Doberstein
Isabell Doberstein
Friedel Dofek
Michelle Doherty
Heidelinde Dolanc
Elisabeth Dolega
Annemarie Doll
Andrea Doller
Corinne Dölling
Ina Domke
Susanne Dopf
Beatrix Dorfmeister
Kathrin Dorfner
Lisa Dorfner
Paula Dorfner
Doris
Claudia Dormann
Marta Dormann
Anja Dörner
Sabine Dorscheid
Stephanie Dörscheln
Franka Dott
Lea Draht
Lazaroula Drakopoulos
Monika Draskovits
Elke Genoveva Dreher
Jutta Dreher
Adelheid Dreistein
Claudia Dreizler
Colette Drescher
Sabine Drescher
Annette Dresel
Angelika Drewes
Eva Droll
Beate Dülks
Claudia Carmen Dullin
Cristina Maria Duna
Isabelle Dural
Sarah Dürr
Hildegard Durst
Barbara Duttle
Margot Duwe

E

Birgit Ebbert
Anne Ebeling
Rita Ebeling
Cosima Eberhard
Petra Eberle
Viviane Ebersold
Franziska Ebert
Regine Ebert
Celina-Jolin Ebinger
Haley Eblinger
Annika Ebner
Edith Ebner
Gertrud Ebner
Magdalena Ebner
Marita Echle
Christine Eck
Elfriede Eck
Sophie Eck
Regina Eckardt
Christa Eckert
Eveline Eckert
Ingrid Eckert
Irmgard Eckert
Eda
Rodica Edelhoff
Brigitte Edelmann
Sibylle Eder
Christa Eekhoff
Efe
Marion Ege
Anike Eggers
Sarah Egli
Andrea Egloff-Natsch
Brigitte Ehler
Birgit Ehrenforth
Wolfrune Ehrenfried
Marleen Ehret
Judith Ehrfeld
Ursula Eiche
Eichendorff-Realschule
 Reutlingen, Klasse 8ac
Maria Eichler
Monika Eichmann

Claudia Eiden
Marlene Eiden
Claudia Eigenmann
Ute Eilemann
Ingrid Eilers
Jasmin Eisele
Ramona Eisele
Isolde Eisele-Colombo
Martha Eisen
Mathilda Eisen
Petra Eisenhauer
Sonja Eisenhofer
Ingeborg Eising
Dagmar Eißler
Elias
Susanne Ell
Katrin Ellinger
Eveline Ellmer
Sandra Elmrich
Diana Elsäßer
Andrea Elsinger
Sonja Elsinger
Brigitte Eltrop
Elsbeth Elwing
Petra Elwing-Wedig
Mona Emamzadeh
Alexandra Embs
Emilia
Sengül Emir
Emma
Emma
Saphira van Empel
Hanna Emrich
Lisa Emrich
Roswitha Endlicher
Elke Endres
Leah Engel
Wiebke Engel
Christine Engelhard
Jutta Engels
Kerim Engin
Monika Engler
Scheyla Englert
Markéta Englich
Marion Engstler
Airon de Jesus Enriquez
 Pereda
Gaby Epple
Yvonne Erb
Petra Erdbrink
Sybille Erdmann-Kille
Tessa von Erdmannsdorff
Birgit Erdrich
Serife Erduhan
Felix Erhardt
Mirjam Erhardt-Böing
Sabine Erkeling-Bruhn
Ursula Erl
Elfie Ernle
Anja Ernst
Anke Ernst
Silke Ernst
Merle Erpenbeck
Mathilde Eschbach
Gerda Eschmann
Louise Espiritu
Stefanie von Essen
Marlis Eßer
Erika Essig
Gertrud Esslinger
Nelly Eßl-Schöll
Christel Eustachi
Eva
Evangelischer
 Krankenpflegeverein
 Ludwigshafen-
 Ruchheim e.V.
Christine Everding
Renate Ewers

F

Angelina Faber
Fides Faber
Mechthilde Faber
Gudrun Fach
Fachhochschule Münster,
 Fachbereich Sozialwesen
Andrea Faisst

Ariane Falk
Ingeborg Falk
Tina Faller
Brigitte Fallert
Familienforum Reutlingen
Lovis Fang
Merlind Fang
Fanny
Julius Färber
Paul Gabriel Farcaș
Felizitas Farrenkopf
Ursula Fasol
Farina Fasse
Petra Faust
Michaela Fechner
Susanne Federschmid
Antje Feenders
Ellen Feigel
Leonard Feigel
Melina Feigel
Martina Feiler
Yvonne Feinsbach
Isabell Feldhaus
Selina Felič
Heike Fengler
Kerstin Fenkner
Leona Ferenczffy
Sibylle Ferner
Alexia Ferrari
Petra Ferreira Goncalves
Hannah Fetter
Karin Fetz
Nadja Fetzer
Renate Fetzer
Liane Feutner
Carmen Feyerabend
Jeanette Fiala
Monika Fiala
Kimberly Fiedler
Maike Fiedler
Nadine Fink
Finn
Amelie-Luise Finzer
Fiona
Monika Fischbach
Amelie Fischer
Anna Fischer
Claudia Fischer
Ellen Fischer
Erika Fischer
Heidi Fischer
Heike Fischer
Lea Fischer
Marie-Eve Fischer
Max Fischer
Renate Fischer
Sabine Fischer
Simone Fischer
Theresa Fischer
Annette Fischer-Rasokat
Franziska Fischler-
   Weickhardt
Daniela Fecker
Brigitte Fleig
Carola Flentje
Sandra Flier
Elvira Flury
Carmen Fochler
Ina Foerster-Köhler
Lauri Föllinger
Daniela Fontana
Förder- und Betreuungs-
   gruppe der WfbM
Beate Formeseyn
Sabine Förschler
Nicole Forster
Elke Förster
Anita Forstner
Karin Franck
Catherine François
Christine François
Malou François
Birgitt Frank
Gabriele Frank
Gudrun Frank
Lucia Frank
Roswitha Frank
Karla Franke

Cathrin Frankenberg
Gabriele Frankowsky
Svenja Fredersdorff
Annette Frei
Berit Frei
Cornelia Frei
Leni Frei
Birgitt Freidel
Freie Schule Lech-Donau,
   Klassen 8+9+10
Freie Waldorfschule
   Offenburg
Sophia Freimark
Ona Freitag
Rose Freudl-Herzog
Freundeskreis Asyl/
   Frauenprojekt
Gerlinde Freundl
Andreas Frey
Anita Frey
Stephanie Frey
Ingrid Friedel
Sabine Friedel-
   Kappelmann
Marianne Friedmann
Christiane Friedrich
Claudia Friedrich
Cornelia Friedrich
Eileen Friedrich
Maria Friedrich
Friedrich-Baur-Grund- und
   Mittelschule, Klassen
   3+4+6
Dagmar Friedrich-Preisler
Maria Friese
Amilia Friesen
Bettina Frink
Christiane Fritsch
Christa Fritz
Heide Fritz
Margit Fritz
Otto Fritz
Annette Fröhlich
Tina Frohne
Ulrike Fromm
Angelika Frühbus
Birgit Frühe
Gabriele Fuchs
Nina Füchsel
Fünf Frauen weben und
   häkeln
Janne Fuhrmann
Fummelclub Sietow
Andrea Fünfstück
Nadine Fünfzig
Anne Funk
Dorothea Funk
Susane Funk
Matilda Funk
Anne-Marie Funken
Margarete Funken-
   Lemke
Martina Fürbach-Weber
Andrea Furch
Annika Furch
Marianne Furrer
Elke Fütterer
Fynn

G

Penelope Gäb
Emilie Gabbert
Gabriele Gäbelein
Christine Gabler
Claudia Gack
Heidi Gadinger-Moser
Theresa Gahr
Regina Galgenmüller
Junita Gampe
Anastasia Gankina
Jessika von Ganske
Anke Ganter-Harsch
Birgit Gardener
Ulrike Gartner
Anja Gartzke
Ute Gasteyer
Anita Gauß
Eva-Maria Gawlik-Sutter

Nicole Gazlig
Pia Gebauer
Rita Gebauer
Sandra Gebauer
Melanie Gebert
Petra Gebhardt
Renate Gebhardt
Dila Gedikli
Buhar Gedo
Gerda Geenen
Inge Geenen
Jennifer Geers
Bettina Gegenheimer
Manuela Gegenheimer
Rosmarie Gegenheimer
Jahin Gehl
Martina Gehring
Ulla Gehring
Dagmar Geiger
Gabriele Geiger
Jutta Geiger
Susanne Geiger
Sibylle Geiges
Gabi Geigle
Birgit Geiselhart
Gabriele Geiß
Dorit Gekle
Stefanie Geldbach
Karin Gelfort
Petra Gelfort
Gemeindebücherei Forst,
   Gruppe "Nadelstunde"
Gemeinschaftsschule
   Freisen, Klasse HUT8
Ricarda Gend
Tanja Gentz
Cäcilia Georgi
Alexandra Gerbenne
Heike Gerbig
Gerda
Susanne Gerdes
Janne Gerdom-Meiering
Christina Gerg
Gerhart-Hauptmann-
   Grundschule Grünheide
   (Mark), Klasse 5c
Jutta Gerlach
Ellen Gerlinger
Irene Gerner-Haug
Daniela Gerstgraser
Sandra Gerstner
Petra Gerstner-Schröder
Lisa T. Gert
Gertrud-Bäumer-
   Berufskolleg, Klassen
   B1E211, B2E211, EVA211
Petra Gewohlies-
   Schwegler
Manna Ghebreigziabiher
Simone Ghovanlou
Xenia Gick
Alexandra Gier
Brunhilde Gierend
Sabine Giersch
Marita Gies
Karin Giese
Sarah Gieseler
Selma Giezer
Greta Giljan
Gudrun Giljan
Bärbel Ginter
Jutta Girrbach
Edeltraud Gismondi
Isolde Glaner
Finnja Gläser
Angelika Glasker
Katjana Gläßer
Elke Glatthaar
Angelika Glatz
Carina Glaw
Ilona Glockner-Huslisti
Eva Glogauer
Annerose Glugert
Irmgard Gnad
Claudia Gnauk

Regina Göbel
Simon Göbel
Lena Maria Gödde
Christa Goede
Petra Goenigk
Daniela Goes
Celine Gögele
Melanie Goik
Ulrike Goldschweer
Azéla Göler
Barbara Goleschny
Jessica Goller
Rita Goller
Ute Iris Goller
Annemarie Göller
Renate Maria Goltz
Amadeo Gomez
Elke Gonser
Shirin Göppert
Evi Göppinger
Ursula Görke
Christa Gorldt
Mona Göschel
Karin Gösmann
Irmgard Gottmann
Sabine Gottschalk-Renk
Elisabeth Gottschick
Clarissa Götz
Marianne Götz
Andrea Götzl
Aaron Götzmann
Daniela Götzmann
Heide Götzmann
Emil Gräber
Ruth Grabherr
Andrea Grabmaier
Gudrun Grabner
Hanna Grabner
Olivia Gradowski
Grafen-von-Sempt-
   Mittelschule Markt
   Schwaben, Klasse 7bm
Anita Grafetstätter
Marie-Anne Grages
Marion Gramer
Anna Grandgeorg Suaréz
Juliane Grass
Gwenda Grässel
Almuth Grätsch
Greenteam ELM-Kids
Eleonora T. Gregor
Gertraud Gregor
Martina Greineisen
Gabriele Greiner
Marie-Luise Greitzke
Diana Grell
Emely Grethler
Lukas Greuter
Wiebke Grevinga
Noah Grewe
Claudia Grewenig
Ingeborg Grießl
Gaby Grigoleit
Angeline Grigorasch
Lara Grill
Sarah Grill
Silke Grimm
Christa Grommelt
Eva-Maria Gröne
Annette Grönewäller
Ruth Gröning
Cornelia Gross
Gerda Gross
Lena Marie Groß
Alexandra Große
Maria Große
Christa Große-Kreul
Anne Grosskost
Ingrid Großmann
Rosemarie Groß-Steinle
Anna-Sophie Grote
Simone Grote
Gabi Grottenthaler
Bridget Grout-Schindler
Lena Gruler
Gisela Grundhöfer
Grundschule Grünwinkel,
   Klasse 3a

Luise Sophia Grunert
Anneliese Grünfelder
Gruppe "Stricken und
   Häkeln" Stuttgart-
   Dürrlewang
Marco Gruschka
Jasmin Gryschka
Noemi Gschwendtner
Lilly-Loreen Gschwind
Christine Gückel-Daxer
Christiane Gulde
Beate Julia Güldener
Britta Güldener-Heinen
Swathi Gunapalan
Elke Günderoth
Havva Günes
Monika Günsche
Doris Günther
Elke Günther
Emely Günther
Ingrid Günther
Louisa Guntrum
Hannelore Güßmann
Diana Guß-Paris
Brigitte Gut
Veronika Güttinger
Christine Guttmann
Gymnasium Achern
   Kunstprofilschule
Gymnasium Oberwil,
   Gruppe JELA

H

Gertrud Haaf
Anna Haag
Uli Haag
Carolin Haas
Christine Haas
Gabriele Haas
Helga Haas
Martina Haas
Silvia Haas
Tanja Haas
Waltraud Haas
Leopold Habanetz
Silvia Häbel
Heidrun Habelt
Bettina Haberland-
   Michel
Anke Habermann
Silke Habich
Julia Hack
Sabine Hack
Christiane Hackel
Barbara Häcker
Marianne Häcker
Max Häcker Grosskost
Helene Hackstein
Maria Haefner
Brigitte Häfner
Elke Häfner
Sabine Hagel
Mechthild Hägele
Andrea Hagen
Elke Hagenlocher
Dagmar Hagenthurn
Andrea Hahlbeck
Ann-Katrin Hahn
Evangeline Hahn
Hannah Katinka Hahn
Banafshe Haidary
Claudia Haider
Viviane Haist
Claudia Hake
Häkelbüdel Heidelberg
Häkel-Nerdys
Hysnije Haljilji
Christiane Haller-Feith
Sandra Hammacher
Ute Hammer-Heinelt
Ines Hampe
Gotlinde Hampen
Sabine Hampl
Doris Hampp
Handarbeitsclub
   Lebenshilfe Mohn
Handarbeitsgruppe
   "Die Doppelmaschen"

Handarbeitsgruppe
   Begegnungsstätte
   Grellstraße 14
Handarbeitsgruppe der
   Lebenshilfe Oberkirch
Handarbeitstreff Mahlberg
Handmade-Treff der
   Gemeindebibliothek
   Mutterstadt
Hanna
Hannes
Nadine Hanschke
Jutta Hansen
Gisela Happel
Susanne Happel
Ulrike Harbers
Stefanie Harders
Hardtstiftung
Hardtwaldschule,
   Klasse 9c
Cora Häring
Martina Harrer
Andrea Harréus
Ewa Harsch
Petra Hartig
Marion Hartinger
Diana Hartmann
Doris Hartmann
Lilian Hartmann
Lina Hartmann
Nadeschda Hartmann
Nisa Carlotta Hartmann
Roswitha Hartmann
Barbara Hartnack
Birgit Hartstein
Marie Harzenetter
Nesrin Hasan
Stephanie Hasslöcher-
   Grimm
Christine Haug
Mira Haumann
Katharina Haupenthal
Tamara Haupt
Nicole Hauptmann
Haus Kunterbunt – Hort an
   der Schule
Irene Hauser
Simone Hauser
Claudia Hauter
Sabine Hauth-Frank
Anna-Lena Hecher
Annette Hecht-Bauer
Marissa Hecker-v. Behr
Brigitte Heeren
Ingrid Heffner
Ella Hegemann
Ingrid Hegenbarth-
   Heinemann
Sigrid Heger
Iris Heiden
Christine Heidmann
Heike
Gabriele Heilig
Margret Heilmann
Edith Heilmeier
Uta-Maria Heim
Leona von Heimburg
Renate von Heimburg
Elke Heimburger
Heimschule Lender
   Sasbach, Klasse 6a
Heimschule Lender
   Sasbach, Kostüm AG
Martina Hein
Sabine Heine
Mika Heinemann
Erika Heinen
Ferdinand Heinen
Friedrich Heinen
Ilka Heinen
Kim Heinrich
Anne Heinrichs
Kerstin Heintzmann
Inge Heinze
Svenja Heinze
Tanja Heinze
Renate Heinzmann
Sabine Heinz-Stempel

Heike Heiß
Johannes Heitkamp
Beatrix Heitz
Cari Helbig
Gabriele Helbing
Leonie Helbing
Alena Held
Tim Christian Heldt
Helena
Helga
Aisha Hellberg
Aaron Helle
Conni Heller
Doris Hellmann
Marita Hellmann
Sigrid Hellweg
Ellen Helmholz
Aletta Helsper
Nina Hemmen
Elfriede Hemmer
Sylvia Hempel
Annette Henke
Eva Henke
Monika Henke
Svenja Hennecke
Andrea Henn-Gangnus
Christin Henning
Monika Hennig
Doris Henning-Schlosser
Inga Hennl-Dib
Marta Henrich
Henry-Benrath-Schule
 Friedberg, WP-Kurs Mode
 und Design
Giulia Marie Henschel
Tamara Henschel
Gabi Hensel
Irina Hensel
Lotte Hensel-Wolf
Edda Henßler
Angelika Hentschel
Kornelia Henzen
Emilie Henzler
Günter Henzler
Sabine Henzler
Traude Henzler
Beate Hepke
Christina Heppke
Margitta Herb
Anette Herbert
Pauline Herbst
Hildegard Herder
Fiona Herdrich
Tina Hering
Vivien Hering
Gabi Hering-Bliesener
Maja Herle
Gabriele Herlyn
Gisela Hermann
Hildegund Hermann
Sonja Hermann
Lea Hernenrath
Beate Herold
Petra Herrlinger
Andrea Herrmann
Joey Kristina Herrmann
Judith Herrmann
Theresia Herrmann
Aurel Hertel
Gaby Hertel
Lucy Hertel
Nelly Hertel
Romy Hertel
Sabine Hertel
Julia Hertweck
Ilona Herzer
Sandra Herzfeld
Christine Herzog
Emily Herzog
Lavinia Herzog
Milane Herzog
Silke Herzog
Manuela Hess
Tina Hesse
Renate Hettel-Schlumberger
Ramona Hetze
Christiane Heubaum
Evemarie Heuckeroth

Selina Heudorfer
Emma Heuldorf
Annette Heumann
Lisanne Heuser
Gabriele Heußer
Christiane von Heyden
Maren Heyer
Hildegard Hiemer
Anni Hilberer
Martina Hilbrandt
Hilda Gymnasium
 Pforzheim, Klasse 7a
Nicole Hildebrandt
Samuel Hildenberg
Lisa Hildenbrand
Dagmar Hillepold
A. Hillert-Zapf
Sylvia Himmel
Margret Himpeler
Reni Hinninger
Alexandra Hinte
Brigitte Hipp
Cora Hirsch
Lea-Michelle Hirsch
Maria Hirsch
Nora Hirte
Paula Hirth
Eva Hirtler
Christiane Hirz
Anny-Marleen Hißbach
Beate Hitschler
Nadine Hlubek
Bao Viet Hoang
Marita Höckendorff
Andrea Hödebeck-Höfig
Britta Hödebeck-
 Schlesinger
Zeinab Hodeib
Gabriele Höfele
Monika Höfels
Birgit Hofer
Elisabeth Hofer
Ilse Hoffmann
Patricia Hoffmann
Ulrike Hoffmann
Verena Hoffmann
Martina Hoffmann
Cornelia Hoffmann-Dodt
Margarete Hofheinz
Claudia Höfler-Neugebauer
Roswith Höfling-Heilig
Gabriele Hofmann
Jutta Hofmann
Luisa Maria Hofmann
Frieda Hofsäß
Heike Hofsäß
Gisela Hoheisel
Heike Höher-Crohn
Anja Hohle
Franziska Hohmann
Sabine Hohmann
Anne Höhn
Johanna Höhn
Claudia Hohnschopp
Inge Hohwarth
Iris Höller
Andrea Hollinderbäumer
Susanne Hollstein
Lea Hollweg
Ineke Holm-van Baren
Christin Holtorf
Maja Holub
Oleksandra Holyaka
Janina Holz
Mechthild Holz
Nara Holz
Maja Holzapfel
Susanne Holzbach
Kathi Holzmann
Johanna Hömke
Denny Hommel
Eveline Honegger
Klara Hönisch
Jacqueline Hoogendoorn
Elisabeth Hoppe
Inge Hoppner
Bärbel Horn
Gertrud Horn

Karin Horn
Malte Horn
Sabine Horn
Jonas Hörner
Petra Hörner
Ursula Hornik
Carmen Hornung
Luise Hornung
Monika Hornung
Hanna Hörtel
Karin Hörtel
Christina Hossner
Nelli Hossner
Barbara Hostalka
Hannah Hottenrott
Mareike Hoyer
Katharina Hubacher
Anna Huber
Elke Huber
Gerda Huber
Irène Huber
Lara Huber
Lydia Huber
Sonja Huber
Lennart Hübler
Eva-Maria Hübner
Mika Elias Hübner
Lioba Huck
Jan Hudarin
Liv Huesmann
Melanie Hufnagel
Hüfnerhaus Beeskow
 "Wolle und Kaffee"
Gabriele van Hülst
Katrin Hultsch
Hildegard Humm
Ulrike Hummel
Leni Hümmeler
Inge Hümmer
Christina Humpert
Elke Hundler
Margit Hunsänger
Julia Hurrle
Doha Husain
Sahra Husain
Jennifer Huschka-Reber
Amina Hushkadamova
Anke Hutt
Gisela Hutzel
Nicole Huwyler
Shi-U Hwang

I

Heike Ibach
Sabine Ibelshäuser
IC Montessori-Montale
Christiane Ihle
Susanne Ihle
Daliah Sarah Ihne
Lisa Ihne
Sarah Ihne
Heike Ihnofeld
Kristin Ilg
Regina Ille-Kopp
Illenau-Werkstätten
Leonie Ilschner
Sabina Ilschner
Ilse
Karla Immenroth
Iris Inderlieht
Helena Ingendae
Inner Wheel Club
 Kraichgau-Stromberg
Barbara Instynski
Irene
Annegret Irrgang
Judith Irrgang
Anita Irsigler
Elisabeth Isaak
Claudia Isele
Lejla Iseni
Andrea Isenmann
Lioba Isensee
Monika Iser
Ademi Iskenderova
Sigrid Istvancsek
Emily Ittenbach
Susanne Ittmann

Andrea B. Ivory
Ines Iwanov

J

Elisabeth Jacobs
Elke Jacqué-Ruby
Sabine Jacubowski
Christa Jäger
Helga Jäger
Martina Jäger
Ursula Jäger
Angelika Jagielo
Edith Jahn
Marion Jahn
Heidemarie Jahnke
Heidi Jahnke
Susanne Jahn-Zihms
Franziska Jakisch
Jana
Helga Janetzko
Sabine Jangner
Heide Janke
Anita Jankowski
Anette Jansen
Therese Jansen
Editha Janson
Nino Janzen
Lena Jäsche
Ahna Jautzer-Braun
Andrea Jelich
Marvin Jeske
Sabine Jess
Karin Jetter
Joan-Miró Grundschule
 Berlin, Klasse 6b
JobKOM-Frauen
 im Mittelpunkt;
 Therapieverbund
 Ludwigsmühle
Johann-Joachim-Becher
 Schule, 1.+2.+3. Lehrjahr
Gudrun Johannsen
Katrin Johannsen
Mara John
Ulrike John
Alice Johnsdorfer
Jonas
Vivian Jones
Ute Jonetat
Felix Jonitat
Ingela Jöns
Bettina Jordan
Heidi Jörg
Gesa Jörgensen-Boumghar
Diana Jörger
Susan Jost
Marita Joussen
Jugendfarm Pfingstweide
Jule
Fabienne Julg
Julian
Frauke Jung
Gudrun Jung
Jeshina Jung
Marion Jung
Sabine Junginger
Ute Jungmann
Petra Jurga
Juane Just
Karoline Jüttner
Henriette Jüttner-Uhlich

K

Rosi K.
Sophie Lisa Kaabi-Egloff
Ilona Kaakschlief
Susanne Kabis
Hanne Kabuth
Andrea Kächelein
Fabian Kaczmarek
Ulrike Kaden
Ursula Kafka-Küng
Johanna Kaim
Brigitte Kaiser
Dagmar Kaiser
Ingrid Kaiser
Lara Kaiser
Margarete Kaiser

Sabine Kaiser
Helga Kalkbrenner
Birgit Kalmutzke
Gisela Kaltschmidt
Susanne Kaltwasser
Sabine Kames
Erika Kamm
Renate Kämmer
Jone Kammerer
Margarete Kammerer
Gabriele Kammergruber
Magdalena Kampf
Sabine Kampf
Doris Kamps
Joleen Kamps
Allison Kaplan
Petra Kapp
Eva Maria Kappes
Heidelore Kappler
Elias Karabiyik
Nisa Karakuyu
Dimitra Karampelia
Kerstin Karasz
Annerose Karcher
Liane Karcher
Birgit Karg
Karin Karle
Hannelore Karpfen
Annemarie Kärsch-Kleine
Josipa Kasalo
Sandra Kascheike
Nicole Kasimirowicz
Elly Kaspar
Anne Käßbohrer
Hedwig Kaster-Bieker
Jutta Kastl
Jutta Kath
Katharina
Katholische Frauengemein-
 schaft Deutschlands,
 Diözesanverband Essen
Katholischer Jugendchor
 Wirbelwind
Katrin
Annelie Kaufmann
Karin Kaufmann
Eva-Maria Krause
Andrea Kautz
Ajna Kavaz
Rosemarie Kayser
Elisabeth Keck
Sabine Keck
Astrid Keller
Emmely Keller
Franziska Keller
Konnie Keller
Marita Keller-Kunigham
Heide Kelly
Linda Kemmer-Landua
Birgit Kempter
Susanne Keppeler
Kerad
Kerim
Barbara Kerkmann
Bianca Kern
Zoe Kern
Marion Kern
Sabine Kern-Drewes
Evelyn Kerner
Sandra Kerschbaum
Melanie Kersken
Ingrid Marie Kesemeyer
Günter Keßler
Ursula Kessler
Michaela Keßler-Oltmanns
Anja Kett
Sophia Kett
Mirija Ketteler
Ameerah Khodaida
Lea Kicherer
Marianne Kieble
Stella Kiebler
Julia Kiefer
Julia Kiemer
Kikos Strickschule
Kilian
Aleyna Kilic
Elanur Kilic

Hira Kilic
Viktoria Kimmel
Agnes Kimmig-Pfeiffer
Hannie de Kinderen
Beate Kindsvater
Melanie Kipfstuhl
Nadiah Kira
Claudia Kircher
Jana Kirchner
Helga Kirk
Sylvia Kirn
Stefanie Kirner
Stephanie Kirner
Hardy Kirstein
Brigitte Kirzlberger
Liza Kis
Heike Kissel-Eltrop
Kiwanis-Frauenclub
 Emmendingen-TARA
Kiyan
Fatma Kiziltas
Irmelin Klaasen van Husen
Monika Klaffs
Klassen "Textiles Gestalten"
 Unterlangenegg
Victoria Kleczka
Kirstin Kleeberg
Annette Klein
Dina Klein
Gisela Klein
Karla Klein
Marion Klein
Monika Klein
Paulina Klein
Susanne Kleinbeck
Elisabeth Kleineheismann
Marion Kleinjans
Karin Klem
Karin Klemenz
Dorothee Klemm
Cornelia Klenkler
Bettina Klemm
Gertrud Kling-Walter
Andrea Klink
Waltraud Klinsing
Holde Klis
Elke Klopottek
Babette Klos
Andrea Klose
Liesel Klotter
Andrea Klotz
Carla Klotz
Ute Klotzbücher
Viola Kluge
Franziska Klumpp
Julian Klumpp
Kaspar Klumpp
Silke Kluth
Magdalena Knab
Gudrun Knapp
Renate Knapp
Petra Knapperzbusch
Bettina Knauber-Huber
Marie Kneer
Miriam Knepper
Sylvia Knewel
Nicola Kniebel
Sabine Knierim
Barbara Maria Knittel-
 Winterfeld
Waltraut Knobloch-Nast
Beate Knoke
Maria Magdalena Knoller
Luzie Knöller
Christiane Knöpfle
Christine Knorr
Susanne Knorr
Barbara Knüchel
Margarete Köbele
Erika Kober
Anna-Lena Koch
Annina Koch
Emma Koch
Julia Koch
Jutta Koch
Karen Koch
Katrin Koch
Kerstin Koch

Nadine Koch
Saskia Koch
Frauke Kochalski
Wiktoria Kochanek
Hannelore Koch-Kahler
Nicoline Koch-Lutz
Melanie Koch-Richner
Finnja Köder
Maja Koebel
Eleonore Koeble
Bettina Koeditz
Dagmar Koerfer-Hauser
Katrin Kofeld
Gilda Kögel
Lisa Kögel
Tina Kögel-Strauß
Gerda Kögler
Sonja Kohl
Julia Kohlbach
Ursula Kohlborn
Fabian Kohler
Peter Kohler
Rita Kohler
Anne Köhler
Charline Köhler
Dorit Köhler
Felicitas Köhler
Gabriele Köhler
Gudrun Köhler
Petra Köhler
Susanne Köhler
Constanze Köhler-Leiß
Monika Kohley
Rosel Kohns
Corinna Kollien
Monika Kollmar
Birgit Kollmar-Thoni
Dorothee Köllner
Kristina Kollwer
Maja Kolm
Regina Kölmel
Damian Konetzka
Angela König
Sabine König
Susanne König
Bahiya Amaya Königsmann
Sibylle Köninger
Christine Konrad
Kathrin Konstanzer
Anna Kopania
Brigitte Kopf
Regina Kopf
Janine-Denise Kopicki
Ute Köppel
Mia Koppenhöfer
Alexandra Korb
Marianne Gabriele
 Kordwittenborg
Renate Körmendy
Steffi Kornhas
Gabriella Kortmann
Diana Kosel
Sabine Verena Koßmann
Christine Köstlin
Barbara Kostyrok
Brigitte Kottke
Alisa Kottmann
Sabine Kraft
Béatrice Krähenbühl
Ilona Krake
Veronika Kral
Gabriele Krämer
Mats Krämer
Silvia Krämer
Susanne Krämer-Rabaa
Ilona Kramesberger
Gertrud Kraschewski
Elo Kratz
Birgit Kratzer
Brigitte Kratzer
Claudia Krause
Dagmar Krause
Erika Krause
Gabriele Krause
Katharina Krause
Manuela Krause
Verena Krause
Irene Krauskopf

Caroline Krauss
Anna Kraut
Sabine Kraut
Brigitte Krawinkel
Ursula Krawinkel
Kreativgruppe der Sozial-
 gemeinschaft Schiltach/
 Schenkenzell e. V.
Kreativgruppe Katholischer
 Frauenverein Aesch BL
Kreativtreff Bürgerverein
 Flehingen e. V.
Kreativtreff Grötzingen
Angela Krebietke
Angelika Krebs
Beatrice Krebs
Carolyn Krebs
Emilia Krebs
Maria Krebs
Heide Krebser-Fögele
Uta Kreher
Anke Krespach
Romy Krespach
Sabine Kreutzer
Verena Kreuz
Imke Kreuzer
Cornelia Krieg
Kerstin Krieg
Nele Emily Krieg
Sylvia Krieg
Luca Krieger
Petra Krieger
Ute Krimmel
Andrea Krimmer
Oskar Kroeker
Mira Krög
Sonja Krög
Barbara Krokowski
Kathrin Kron
Uta Kronauer
Margret Kronberg
Noah Krönert
Susanne Kronthaler
Jitka Kropp
Silke Kropp
Sabine Kröselberg
Linda Krötz
Karl Krug
Beate Krüger
Elke Krüger
Sabine Krüger
Sven Krüger
Rita Brunhilde Krumes
Marianne Krup
Max Krusche
Renate Krüßmann
Susanne Krust
Gabi Kübler
Petra Kübler
Kubus³ e. V. + ArTik e. V.
Carola Küchler
Heidi Kugel
Margarethe Kugler
Waltraud Kugler
Sabine Kühhirt
Pia Kuhlmann
Sidney Kuhn
Anneliese Kühn
Birgit Kühn
Christiane Kühnen
Hanna Kühnle
Julian Kühnle
Lukas Kühnle
Birgit Kühr
Marlene Kulke
B. Kull
Claudia Kull
Renate Kullmann-Bragulla
Zoe Kumm
Mylène Kümmerling
Anette Kumpf
Helga Kunemann
Christine Küng
Kunsthof Klapfenberg
Emilia Kuntz
Nico Kuntz
Barbara Küntzler
Katja Kunz

Linda Kunz
Petra Kunz
Ulrike Kunz
Ilona Kunze-Concewitz
Gerdi Kunzelmann
Franziska Küper
Mathis Küper
Mylo Kupfer
Editha Kurfürstová
Barbara Kurka-Nußbaum
Andrea Kurlanda
Meltem Kurnova
Katja Kurpjuweit
Jannik Kurz
Anja Kürzel
Melanie Kuschel
Viona Kussmaul
Britta Kuth
Ingrid Küttinger
Doreen Kwauka
Angela Kym

L

Michaela Lächele-
 Frauenschuh
Hannah Lachetta
Jutta Lachner
Susanne Lachnit
Hanna Lack
Bärbel Lagies
Ute Lahann
Margarete Laible
Bea Lambert
Lotte Lambert
Luzie Lambert
Eva-Maria Lamberty
Heike Lambrecht
Judita Lampe
Inge Lampen
Magalie Lampert
Charlotte Lamprecht
Renate Landerer
Elke Lang
Krista Lang
Petra Lang
Amilia Lange
Ursula Lange
Vera Lange-Jauch
Evi Langendorf-Jauch
Johannes Langenhövel
Ulrike Langenstein
Jakob Langer
Regina Lange-
 Wohlschlager
Karen Langguth
Sarah Langhammer
Marta Längin
Nadine Langmaack
Christine von Langsdorff
Nadja Lapicz-Kummerow
Françoise Laspeyres
Elke Latendorf
Vincenzina Lattuca
Petra Lauer
Simone Lauhof
Anja Laumbacher
Birgit Lawrenz-Pollmann
Beate Lay
Anna Lazzaro
LDT NAGOLD Akademie
 für Modemanagement
Sylvie Le Boucher
Learning English Forever
Lebenshilfe e. V. Werk-
 stätte Bühl
Lebenshilfe Stuttgart-
 Möhringen, Wohnanlage
 Probstsee
Bettina Leclaire
Thomas Leclaire
Elke Lederer
Sarah Leenen
Christine Lehmann
Helga Lehmann
Susanne Lehnert
Sabine Lehnguth
Gabriele Lehnhof-Menn
Marie-Luise Lehr

Lehrer des Max-Planck-
 Gymnasium
Luise Leibold-Nathal
Brigitte Leicht
Silke Leicht
Sonja Leicht
Beate Leier
Tina Leingang-Schwab
Judith Leinhos
Susanne Leininger
Jana Leipold
Annika Leistikow
Lena
Birgitta Lenhoff
Liliane Leniere-Reus
Annabell Lenschow
Claudia Lenz
Susanne Lenz
Tanja Lenz
Marie-Sophie Leonhard
Nina Leonhard
Regina Leonhart
Cornelie Leopold
Daniela Leopold
Alea Lerch
Dorota Lesniowska
Martina Lessio
Angela Lett
Maria Theresia Lettner
Evi Silvia Leu
Ulrike Leuchtner
Karin Leue
Verena Leusch
Petra Lever
Margitta Levy
Ilona Lewanski
Angela Leyder
Luise Leyendecker
Anja Leyhausen
Annelies Lichtenegger
Angela Lichtenthäler
Inge Lichter
Johanna Lieb
Mia Melody Liebhold
Tanja Liebmann
Marion Liehr
Evelyne Lienhardt
Edeltraud Lier
Carina Linde
Andrea Linden
Kornelia Lindenlauf
Friederike Lindenmaier
Anita Lindenmann
Petra Lindenmeyer
Lilly Lindenthal
Hannelore Linder
Bastian Linderl
Cora Lindner
Hannah Lingel
Veronika Lingenfelder
Andrea Link
Diana Link
Helga Linke
Samira Linke
Anja Linker
Dagmar Linnert
Katja Lippert
Magdalena Lipscher
Lisa
Lise-Meitner-Gymnasium,
 Klasse 5a, Bildende Kunst
Lina Lißner
Sabine Lißner
Kristel Lleshi
Elgin Löbbecke
Samuele Locatelli
Ulrike Loch
Heike Lochow
Tanja Loderhose
Petra Loguercio
Monika Loh
Marie Lohmann
Susanne Lohmann
Carmen Lohrmann
Barbara Lohse
Natalie Lombardo
Frieda Lörch
Lorelai

Anna Lorenzen
Angelika Lotterer
Birgit Lotz
Louisa
Sylvia Lubinski
Luca
Waltraud Lucius
Rosemarie Lück
Karla Lückertz-Lukosch
Antje Ludin
Rahel Susanna Luft
Gudrun Lühr
Alisa Lukacevic
Katrin Lukei
Kalina Lulcheva
Manuela Lumpp
Gudrun Lung
Sibylle Lurz
Käte Lüthi
Nina Lüthi
Dani Lüttich
Anna-Maria Lutz
Anja Lützel
Andrea Lutz-Krämer

M

Brigitte Maag
Romana Mach
Ruth Mack
Monika Mack-Fischer
Mädchentreff der
 Waldkirche Lenggries
Brigitte Mäder
Maria Madlener
Magnus
Andrea Mahler-Rink
Anneliese Mahr
Marianne Mahr
Anja Maier
Annette Franziska Maier
Gudrun Maier
Philipp Maier
Sabine Maier
Dagmar Mailand
Susanne Maile
Babette Mairoth-
 Voigtmann
Christa Majer-Kachler
Valeria Majorov
Milana Malorodow
Conny Mang
Martina Mangels
Renate Mangler
Sonja Mann
Nina Mannes
Manon Mannherz
Gabriele Manz
Renate Maor
Marijana Marcic
Andrei Marian
Maria-Ward-Schule Bad
 Homburg
Hanna Marie
Marie
Gabriela Mark
Markgraf-Ludwig-
 Gymnasium, Schülerinnen
 der Klasse 7c
Frau Marschar
Edith Marterer
Beate Marterer-Schweiger
Annalena Martin
Maria Martin
Nike Martiné
Heide Marutschke
Anne Marx
Helena Maryniok
Maschinistins Strick-
 guerilla
Elvira Mäske
Christian Massier
Claudia Masson
Anja Masuch
Sergio Mateo
Marina Mateska
Daniela Matschke
Christel Mattes-Pyttlich
Amelie Maucher

Bärbel Mauderer
Gisela Mauer
Max
Maximilian
Maya
Edeltraud Mayer
Kerstin Mayer
Roswitha Mayer
Elfie Mayer-Fulde
Marliese Mayer-Götz
Karin Mayerlen
Irene Mayer-Martin
Brigitte Mayr-Seidl
Sabine Meenen
Birgit Meerkamp
Leonie Meerkamp
Sarah Meerkamp
Ruth Mees-von Bernstorff
Fulvia Mega
Ursula Mehler
Uschi Mehler
Dagmar Mehlhorn-
 Schmidt
Erina Mehmetaj
Katharina Mehr
Andrea Meier
Astrid Donata Meier
Isabell Meier
Mandy Meier
Sabine Meier
Sina Meier
Tirza Meier-Oser
Sarah-Charline Meiners
Marion Meininger
Jana Meister
Sabine Meister
Selina Melcher
Sophie Melcher
Tanja Melcher
Elina Melito
Edith Melone
Irmgard Mende
Frederik Mengel
Susanne Menges
Roswitha Menke
Margret Menkhaus
Sibylle Menneking
Mechtild Menzel
Michaela Menzel
Anna Merhart
Johanna Mering
Joana Merk
Susanne Merke
Ilsemarie Merkel
Brigitte Merkle
Sigrid Merkle
Valentina Merkus
Grit Merten
Jutta Mertens
Martina Mertesacker
Maren Mertins
Gisela Mertsch
Elke Merx-Fischer
Janine Méry
Katja Merz
Gabi Merz-Palleis
Ursula Meschede
Jonah Messerle
Martina Messing
Simone Messing
Ingrid Methner
Lena Metz
Lisa Metz
Corinna Metzger
Susanne Metzger
Margot Metzinger
Monika Metzler
Kathrin Metz-Veyhl
Rosemarie Meyberg
Ameli Meyer
Carolin Meyer
Christel Meyer
Gudrun Meyer
Irmgard Meyer
Paula Meyer
Tanja Meyer
Jule Meyermann
Irmgard Meyer-Steinhart

Mia
Silvia Micalizzi
Michael
Anne-Elisa Michaeli
Michelberg Gymnasium,
  Klasse 7c + 8b
Helga Middelberg
Ute Middelstorb
Annette Mielke
Petra Mies
Beate Mieslinger
Eva Miguet
Tim Miksch
Cordula Mildenberger
Beatrix Millies
Judith Millinger
Cornelia Milto
Melina-Sophie Minke
Somaya Miri
Marit Missel
Mit Herz – von Hand e.V.
Mittelschule Hittisau,
  Klassen 2a + 2b
Mittelschule Höchst,
  Klasse 2
Susanne Mitterwieser
Mittwochskurs der
  Begegnungsstätte am
  St. Carolushaus
Mjellma
Ingrid Möck
Rita Mocnik
Modefachschule
  Sigmaringen
Modestudio Piaskovy
Annette Mödinger
Anneliese Mohr
Brigitte Mohr
Doris Mohr
Uta Möhr
Franziska Möker
Katja Moldenhauer
Heike Möllendorf
Gisela Möllers
Manuela Möllinger
Natalia de Monasterio
  Schrader
Regina Montesano
Heidi Monttet
Wanja Mörbel
Moritz
Hannah Moschina
Annabell Moser
Katja Moser
Renate Moskal
Marion Mosler
Gaby Mössner
Houda Mrad
Renate Mrusek
Ulrike Mühlbayer-Gässler
Bodil Mühlenbrock
Maja Mühlethaler
Corinna Muhsal
Carmen Muley
Lucia Muley
Alexandra Müller
Angela Müller
Birgit Müller
Bosiljka Müller
Brigitte Müller
Brunhild Müller
Chayenne Müller
Christina Müller
Cornelia Müller
Daniela Müller
Elke Müller
Flora Müller
Gitta Müller
Heidrun Müller
Hildegard Müller
Jasmin Müller
Julia Müller
Kerstin Müller
Leni Müller
Magret Müller
Merle Müller
Mia Müller
Monika Müller

Nelli Müller
Patricia Müller
Paul Müller
Renate Müller
Ruth Müller
Susann Müller
Susanne Müller
Tanja Müller
Una Müller
Yannis Müller
Eva Müller-Dürrschmidt
Gioia Müller-Russo
Ruth Müller-Schär
Joy Müller-Thoma
Irene Müller-Wittner
Petra Müllner
Horst Mund
Birgit Mungenast
Ursula Munz
Angelika Murano
Martina Murray
Manuela Mussong
Helga Mutter
Amelie Muyldermans

N

Anja Nagel
Jessica Nagel
Jutta Nagel
Birgit Nägele
Johanna Nägele
Hannelore Nagels
Nähxt GmbH, Das kreative
  Stoffhaus
Ute Napientek
Leah Nass
Katja Naumann
Sabine Naumann
Jamila Nawra
Claudia Necker
Beate Nedović
Anna Neidhart
Oliwia Nejman
Nelly
Andrea Nentwig
Susanne Nerlich
Uschi Neroladakis
Dörte Neßler
Annett Neßmann
Gabriele Nesyt
Martina Netzer
Samira Neuber
Erika Neubig
Claudia Neuen
Rita Neugart
Claudia Neugebauer
Annette Neumair
Kerstin Neumann
Lotti Neumann
Vera Neureuther
Sonja Neus
Gabriele Ney
Miriam Ney
Ngoc Tram Anh Nguyen
León Nibbering Mancebo
Carina Nickel
Lotte Niebling
Ursula Nied
Carolin Niederalt
Björn Niederhöfer
Annika Niemeyer
Nikolaus-von-Myra-Schule
  Philippsburg, Klasse 7 und
  Häkel-AG
Brigitte Nimmrich
Sabine Ningel
Manja Noach
Verena Nobel
Claudia Nold
Christa Nölke, kfd DV Essen
Sabine Nöltner
Noor
Nora
Johanna Nord
Tobias Nordmann
Nordschule Neureut,
  Klasse 4a
Heike Nowatschka-Muhlack

Anita Nüsse
Helga Nusser
Elsbeth Nusser-Lampe

O

Janine Obendorf
Claudia Oberdörfer
Cornelia Obergföll
Filina Oberle
Kristina Obermair
Barbara Ochsenreither
Elke Ocker
Cordula Odenthal
Katrin Oehlert
Ursula Oelke
Arwen Oelkers
Gisela Oeß-Langford
Regina Oesterling
Petra Offermanns
Christl Öhler
Frau Öhlrich
Brigitte Ollesch
Sabine Olschner
Elisabeth Olschowsky
Gundi Omlor
Elena Onken
Anna Opferkuch
Katerina Opferkuch
Katharina Ortel
Renate Ortner
Claudia Oser
Mina Oshnouei
Marion Oßwald
Brigitte Ostertag
Margarete Ostrowski
Doris Ott
Ingrid Ott
Irene Ott
Marius Ott
Anne-Bärbel Ottenschläger
Liv Otterbach
Michaela Ottnad
Ute Otto
Gisela Otto-Distler
Otto-Schott-Gymnasium
  Mainz-Gonsenheim
Marianne Otzko
Bettina Overath
Liva Özdogan
Ali Özmen

P

Henny P.
Susanne Pably
Doreen Pabst
Birgit Padberg
Maria Pages
Annemarie Paiani
PAMINA Schulzentrum,
  Schüler des Wahlpflichtfachs
  Kommunikationsdesign
Kathrin Panidis
Eleni Pantazidou
Celina Panther
Gisela Panter
Mara Panter
Meike Panter
Ute Papadopoulos
Dafni Papandreou
Eva Papp
Kerstin Paries
Marion Parsch
Pascal
Johanna Paschen
Ronja Paschen
Patchwork Gruppe Achern
Dagmar Patt
Alexandra Pätzelt
Eva Pätzold
Susanne Pätzold
Liora Paul
Ursula Paul
Paula
Regine Pauls
Susanne Paulus
Eva Paur
Birgit Pavelka
Barbara Pawelk

Miriam Peitgen
Ulla Peithner
Marlies Pellenz
Margit Pelz
Luca Noel Pempe
Beate Penz
Angelika Peplinski
Sabine Perez
Lucia Perocco
Annemarie Persson
Agnes Peter
Jennifer Peter
Cordula Peter
Kornelia Peterka
Renate Peterka
Barbara Peters
Gina Peterson
Ilijas Petonjic
Gabi Petri
Ute Petsch
Petra-Maria Petzoldt
Ute Pfähler
Ilse Pfaudler
Silke Pfeifer
Alexa Pfeiffer
Gabriele Pfeiffer
Mia Pfeiffer
Patrick Pfeiffer
Vanessa Pfeiffer
Daria Pfingsten
Peggy Pfitzer
Paul Pflüger
Angelika Pfrang-Kempf
Philip
Sandra Philipitsch
Anne Philipp
Veronika Philipps
Nadja Pidan
Frederike Pienkoß
Heike Pienkoß
Christel Pietschmann
Franziska Pietschmann
Adelheid Pilder
Katrin Pinkel
Ursula Pirker
Angelika Pischke
Anja Piteur
Nicole Pitha
Cassandra Plaikner
Edeltraut Plankensteiner
Ulrike Plath
Annika Platte
Marielle Pletsch
Agnes Pliester
Martina Podlewski
Melissa Pogoda
Britta Pohland
Susanne Polewsky
Erika von Polheim
Alessia Poli
Anne Pollak
Claudia Polzhuber
Patricia Polzhuber
Elena Pomohaci
Beate Pons
Gertraud Ponschab
Monika Ponzelar
Maria Ponzo
Magdalena Popp
Ginger Portele
Veronika Pösel
Maren Pötther
Praxisvollschule PPH-
  Augustinum
Roswitha Pregger
Edith Preis
Nicole Prenger
Doris Presler
Angelika Prestenbach
Birgit Prestenbach
Katrin Pribbernow
Daria Pricopi
Stefanie Prießnitz
Birgit Pries-Wächter
Sylvia Prillwitz
Primarschule Selzach
Sabine Prinz
Paula Probst

Sabine Probst
Simone Probst
Anke Proft
Elke Prokop
Nicole von Prondzinski
Annette Pross
Gisela Pugni Spatz
Jonna Püschel
Christine Putz
Stefanie Pütz
Dawina Pyka

Q

Irina Quast

R

Gabriele Radke
Monika Rager-Thomer
Ursula Rahmes
Uta Raible
Kathrin Räker
Heidrun Ramaker
Marie-Luise Ramle
Mahek Rana
Gerlinde Raphael
Antonia Rapp
Rappenbügler Strickliesl
Bärbel Rapporlie
Gerlinde Rasper
Stephanie Rastätter
Frau Rath
Sandra Rath
Barbara Rau
Karin Rau
Susanne Rauch
Ingrid Raulien
Gabriele Rauner
Martina Rausch
Dorothee Rauschenberger
Michaela Rauscher
Siglinde Rebstock
Eva Rech
Vera Rech
Aloisia Rechberger
Tara Kristina Reddi
Sabine Reese-Blumentrath
Melanie Regelmann
Sylvia Regler
Mechthild Regner
Hildegard Rehm
Svenja Rehse
Silke Reibeling
Margot Reich
Michael Reichenbach
Susanne Reichenbach
Gerrit Reichert
Micky Reichle
Hille Reick
Jonas Reifinger
Hieke Reijnhoudt
Uschi Reimann
Laura Reina
Nicole Reiner
Priscilla Reiner
Louisa Reinert
Bianka Reinhardt
Anja Reinhold
Sibylle Reis
Marianne Reisch
Irene Reise
Rosemarie Reisinger
Barbara Reiss
Lisa Annemarie Reiß
Rico Reiß
Susan Reiss
Elisabeth Reißig
Charlotte Reiter
Beate Reitnauer
Andreas Relitz
Ingrid Renner
Michaela Renz
Monika Rettig
Margarete Rettkowski-Felten
Birgit Reusch
Monika Reuß
Gabriele Reuther
Jeannette Rheinländer
Meike Rheinschmitt

Anette Richter
Grit Richter
Jutta Richter
Susanne Richter
Petra Richtsteig
Helga Riebe
Marion Riebschläger
Andreas Riedinger
Britta Riedmann
Eike Riegel-Heitbrink
Bärbel Rieger
Nina Rieger
Ursel Rieger
Stephanie Riemer
Susanne Riesterer-Koch
Sibylle Riffel
Christiane Righetti
Eva Rigsinger
Ilze Rimicane
Brigitte Rinck
Clara Rinck
Susanne Rinck
Christel Rindt
Lina Ringwald
Heike Rist
Rosemarie Rist
Kirsten Ritter
Marie-Christin Rittinger
Barbara Rittmeier
Ursula Rittmeier
Birgit Rixius
Robert-Bosch-
  Gesamtschule Hildesheim
Doris Roberts
Gitta Röckel
Marion Rockenmaier
Elisabeth Röckl
Britta Rodefeld
Susanne Röder
Wilhelm Röder
Susanne Röder-Wittl
Christiane Rödling
Bianca Rohe
Katrin Rohland
Lisa Rohling
Annette Röhling
Martina Rohnacher
Ute Röhnisch
Dagmar Röhrbein
Sybille Rohrmann
Aude Rohwer
Mira Rohwer
Silke Rokitta
Astrid Roland
Christiane Roller
Patricia Romeis
Christine Röminger
Anke Roos
Rosa
Stefanie Rösch
Emma Roscher
Annette Rosenboom
Ute Rosenfeld
Elisa Rosenkranz
Birgit Ross
Ulrike Rößler
Brigitte Rößler-Gebhard
Ulrike Rossmy
Dorothea Roters
Julia Roth
Leonie Roth
Maria Roth
Tanja Roth
Ulrike-Julia Roth
Ursula Roth
Ute-Monika Roth
Hanna Rothenbücher
Jana Rothenhöfer
Gerhild Rother
Dina Rothfuß
Martina Rothley
Anke Rothmüller
Julia Rottmayer
Antonia Rotzoll
Maria Rudek
Evelyn Rudolf
Diana Rudys
Mirjam Ruegger

Linda Rüegsegger
Regina Rügammer
Lina Ruggiero
Christel Ruh
Carla Ruhland
Odeke Ruhland
Kathrin Rühlow
Astrid Rupertus
Christine Rupp
Claudia Rupp
Sarina Rupp
Ulrike Rupp
Sabine Ruppert
Brita Rüsseler
Maxim Russu
Gabi Ruth
Ruth-Weiss-Realschule
Aschaffenburg

S

Marlene Sachse
Verena Sachse
Erika Sager
Marianne Sagerer-
Eichinger
Karin Sahm
Bassam Sahmini
Daniela Saiger
Maren Saiger
Birgit Sailer
Samantha Salewski
Brigitte Salhöfer
Salih
Verena Salomon
Beate Salzer
Ekaterina Salzmann
Vera Salzmann
Jana Samoilenco
Rio Fernandes Sampaio
Giovanna Sampietro
Lion Samson
Annette Sand
Martina Sander
Petra Sander
Marlis Sandholzer
Sandra
Sinje Sanft
Solvejg Santen
Monika Sanwald
Sara
Jana Sarai
Hatice Sari
Christina Sarnes
Anneliese Sarter
Elke Sarter
Lara Tuana Sartor
Zara Melisa Sartor
Charlotte Sartorius
Viola Sartorius
Jona Sattler
Karla Sattler
Andrea Sattler-Klein
Andrea Sauer
Anne Sauer
Birgit Sauerwald
Brigitte Sausele
Walburga Sausner
Claudia Sax
Inge Schaaf
Margit Schaal
Gundula Schaar
Lieselotte Schaber
Barbara Schach
Daniela Schach
Birgit Schade
Inge Schade
Martina Schädlich
Jutta Schaeffer
Sonia Schaeffer
Antje Schaer
Birgit Schäfer
Brigitte Schäfer
Heike Schäfer
Key-Key Schäfer
Mechthild Schäfer
Naemi Schäfer
Regina Schäfer
Robin Schäfer

Susanne Schäfer
Anna-Maria Schäfer-Keck
Astrid Schall
Birgit Schall
Birgit Schaller
Rose-Marie Schallnus
Birgit Schanz
Tatjana Schanz
Katharina Scharfe
Susanne Schaude
Dorothea Schäufele
Helga Schauseil
Brigitte Schauwienold
Helga Schavoir
Alia Scheck
Helga Scheele
Sabrina Scheffler
Finja Scheib
Hannah Scheid
Giulia Scheller
Nadia Scheller
Stella Scheller
Sabine Schellhorn
Margarita Schemel
Heike Schene
Juliane Schene
Sabine Scherbaum
Kirsten Scherer
Julia Scherr
Marie-Luise Scherrer
Eva Schertenleib
Elke Scheske
Maria Schetter-Fluor
Susanne Scheuermann
Anita Scheurer
Daniela Scheyhing
Angela Schickler
Karin Schifferer
Elke Schiffler
Rena Schiller
Svenja Schiller
Katja Schilling
Roman Schilling
Manuela Schillinger
Barbara Schindler
Franca Schindler
Hendrik Schindler
Julia Schindler
Renate Schindler
Sabine Schindler
Sandra Schindler
Susanne Schindler
Hilde Schipf
Diana Schischkalov
Anna Schlachter
Lena Schlatterer
Petra Schlegel
Renate Schlegel
Pia Schleh
Gisela Schleißinger
Michaela Schlemper
Carlotta Schlesinger
Ute Schlindwein
Jutta Schlinke
Doris Schlitz-Salvado
Ursel Schloeder-Weck
Sivia Schlör
Simone Schlosser
Michael Schlösser
Juline Schlüter
Rosemarie Schlüter
Luisa Schmahl
Ines Schmauder
Inge Schmehr
Franziska Schmeling
Andrea Schmid
Carmen Schmid
Chantal Schmid
Rosi Schmid
Bärbel Schmider
Alexandra Schmidt
Angela Schmidt
Antonia Schmidt
Barbara Schmidt
Beatrix Schmidt
Christel Schmidt
Christlinde Schmidt
Claudia Schmidt

Cornelia Schmidt
Gudrun Schmidt
Kara Schmidt
Karin Schmidt
Katica Schmidt
Nathalia Schmidt
Paul Schmidt
Ulrike Schmidt
Vera Schmidt
Verena Schmidt
Ingrid Schmidtke
Gabriele Schmidt-Wurth
Annette Schmitt
Barbara Schmitt
Christina Schmitt
Helene Schmitt
Katja Schmitt
Nidzara Schmitt
Ursula Schmittele
Gabriele Schmitt-Horneff
Doris Schmitz
Heike Schmitz
Regina Schmuker
Katharina Schmutterer
Cornelia Schmutz
Barbara Schnabel
Birgitta Schnaibel
Tina Schnapka
Alexandra Schneble-
Schutter
Marina Schneeberger
Irmgard Schneid
Anette Schneider
Christina Schneider
Conny Schneider
Doreen Schneider
Edeltraud Schneider
Ellen Schneider
Hannah Schneider
Hannelore Schneider
Henriette Schneider
Irmgard Schneider
Martina Schneider
Petra Schneider
Regina Schneider
Renate Schneider
Sabine Schneider
Sieglinde Schneider
Stefanie Schneider
Ulrike Schneider
Veronika Schneider
Beate Schneider-Hättich
Barbara Schneiderheinze
Daniela Schneider-Schrode
Lisanne Schneider-Schwarz
Greta Emilia Schnell
Marlis Schnell
Heike Schneller
Eva Schniedertüns Gornik
Linnea Schnürer
Greta Schnurr
Sophie Marie Schnurre
Monika Schoder
Renate Schoenmakers
Hannah Schoh
Kirsten Schölling
Samuel Schollmeyer
Thora Scholz
Sabine Schön
Frauke Schondelmaier
Petra Schöne
Elisabeth Schönert
Nicole Schönholzer
Karin Schöninger
Gundrun Schork
Tina Schrade
Barbara Schramm
Ida Schratzenstaller
Birgit Schreiber
Silke Schreiber
Sunny Schreiber
Andrea Schreiner-
Gagsteiger
Marie-Luise Schreyer
Cornelia Schröder
Ida Schröder
Martina Schröder
Stefanie Schröder

Hannelore Schubert
Patricia von Schuckmann
Kathrin Schuh
Marie Sophie Schuh
Marlene Schuh
Sibylla Schuldt
Maren Kristin Schüle
Schülerhaus Grundschule
Zazenhausen, Klassen 3+4
Schülerhort Weinbrenner-
straße
Schülerinnen und Schüler
der Fritz-Nuss-Schule,
Olgahospital Stuttgart
Sandra Schüller
Finja Marie Schulte
Kathrin Schulte
Zoe Schulte
Helene Schultz
Sabine Schultze
Anita Schulz
Martina Schulz
Mia Schulze
Sieglinde Schulz-Krieg
Anneliese Schumacher
Jana Schumacher
Josy Schumacher
Monika Schumacher
Ria Schumacher
Anneliese Schumacher-
Piel
Annerose Schumann
Christine Schumann
Christa Schunk
Maria Schürmeyer
Susi Schuster
Allmut Schütze
Leni Schwab
Maria Schwabbauer
Laetitia Mercedes Schwall
Antje Schwan
Johanna Schwan
Sabine Schwarte
Mina Schwarz
Mona Schwarz
Petra Schwarz
Regina Schwarz
Sabine Schwarz
Niklas Schwarzer
Melinda Schwarzer-Papp
Ursula Schwarzwälder
Luisa Marie Schwee
Claudia Schweikert Zeugin
Natalie Schweikert Zeugin
Gerda Schweiß
Niklas Schweizer
Susanne Schweizer
Stefanie Schwemmer
Ursula Schwendenmann
Susanne Schwerdtfeger
Josie Schwerling
Inge Schwientek
Waltraud Schwill
Petra Schwill-Elling
* Margaretha Schwind
Tina Schwöbel
Gabriele Schwörer
Monika Schwörer
Martina Sebold
Elke Sebsle
Gaby Seeger
Milla Marlene Seel
Birgit Seger
Johanna Segmüller
Marion Seibel
U. A. Seibert
Mireille Seibt
Claudia Seiderer
Liane Seidl-Lang
Brigitte Seifried
Elvira Seiler
Monika Seiler
Sabine Seither
Evelyn Seiverth
Karin Selic
Elisabeth Selig
Rosa Maria Sellen
Ursula Sendelbach

Anne Sengpiel
Seniorenstift Mandelberg
Annette Sense
Margarete Sepúlveda
Marah Setinc
Annette Setz
Michaela Setzler
Maxi Seybold
Mona Seyferth
Falko Seyffarth
Mary Shaburishvili
Aziz Shila
Annette Sibbing-Hurler
Gudrun Siebel
Lucas Siedelmann
Doris Siefert
Helga Siefert
Hanne Siefert-Reimann
Susanne Siegmann
Ulla Siemes
Ute Siepelt
Helga Sievers
Ruth Siewe
Lucien Siewerin
Lena Signer
Andrea Silber
Frau Silber
Heike Simon
John-Luca Simon
Martina Simonis
Ruth Sina-Liedtke
Regina Sindermann
Petra Sinn
Viola Sinn
Jane Sinner
Susanne Sippel
Petra Sitter
Carmen Sitter-Kotz
Tabea Sitzmann
Heidi Skirde
Lysann Skrabin
Lydia Skroch
Brigitte Slavicek
Jurina Slavicek
Milina Slynicyn
Gertraude Smekal
Courtenay Smith
Katrin Sneschko
Merle Sobbeck
Rita Söhn
Helen Sohns
Pia Sohns-Riedl
Katharina Sokiran
Renate Solich
Monika Sollberger
Heike Sölter
Andrea Sommer
Antje Sommer
Birgit Sonnhof
Bettina Sonntag
Karin Sonntag
Kordula Sonntag
Christel Sonntag-
Augenstein
Soroptimist International
Deutschland, Club Murgtal
Laura Sorrentino
Sonja Sorrentino
Ina Söther
Soziotherapie Deutscher
Orden, Haus Waldherr
Fadilete Spahiu
Gabriele Spaltuer
Claudia Spandl-Richter
Oskar Spangenberger
Heike Spann
Karin Spannagel
Elfriede Spanowski
Corinna Späth-Guerdane
Johanne Späth-Winnen
Sabine Speck
Tina Speck
Birgitt Spendler
Christiane Nana Spengler
Melanie Spiegel
Petra Spieß
Berta Spissinger
Claudia Splitthoff-Drescher

Dagmar Spohn
Lisa Sporer
Martina Spörl
Anna-Lena Sprenger
Brigitte Springer
Cornelia Springer
Eva-Maria Springer
Susanne Srajek-Erdugan
Irina-Daniela Ssmoller
Erdmute Stachlewitz
Maria Stachnik
Maria Stadler
Sandra Stadler
Carla Stadtmüller
Christa-Maria Stahl
Sabine Stahlkopf
Ina Stallbörger
Maria-Theresia Stamm
Helga Stampfl
Monika Stampfl
Angelika Stanior
Michaela Stanior-
Frankenberger
Carolin Stanior-Räuchle
Katarzyna Stanska
Waltraud Stapf
Adelheid Stark
Bettina Stark
Jeanette Stark
Hilde Starke
Andrea Stark-Engelhardt
Beatrice Staub
Catherine Staub
Tessa Staudenmaier
Bärbel Staudenmayer
Monika Stegemann
Kristina Stehr
Annette Steimle
Sabine Stein
Heike Steinbrenner
Lara Steiner
Ulrike Steiner-Bühler
Stefanie Steiner-Grage
Marianne Steinert
Daniela Steinfeld
Marius Steinkämper
Andrea Steinmeyer
Carola Steitz
Nina Stelzner Gil
Heike Stemmle
Hanne Marie Stender
Karen Stender
Meike Stender
Frida Stengeler
Nele Stenger
Jutta Stephan
Martina Stern
Petra Steudle
Joanna Stevenson
Irene Stich
Stich- und Strickgruppen
Idstein
Helma Stichler
Kerstin Stiefel
Antje Stierle
Annemarie Stillger
Florentine Stix
Karin Stober
Heidelinde Stober-
Ehrhardt
Andrea Stock
Caroline Stocker
Filippa Stockhammer
Ursula Stöckmann
Stephanie Stöhr
Yasmin Stöhr
Susanne Stoldt
Christina Stoll
Stefanie Stolle
Inge Stollhof
Susanne Stooß
Heike Stoschek
Annette Stotz
Margarete Straub-Ott
Petra Strauch
Dorit Streb
Anja Strehlow
Eva Streich

Strick & Faden-Gruppe, Mehrgenerationenhaus Schönefeld der Kindheit e.V.
Strick-Club Neuenbürg/ Straubenhardt
Strickclub Schwesternschaft der gefallenen Maschen
Strickkreis Forum Dunningen/Mauch
Strickliesel Team
Stricktreff Landfrauen RSKN Esslingen
Martina Striebel
Notburga Stripf
Ellen Strnadl
Barbara Stroh
Heidi Ströhemann
Ruth Stromberg
Hildegard Struck
Wiktoria Strycharz
Daniela Stuber
Max Stuck
Studierende der Oberkurse der Evangelischen Fachakademie für Sozialpädagogik in Schweinfurt
Maria Stühler
Almut-Elfi Stühmeier
Susanne Sturm
Vera-Birgitt Stutz
Amanda Stützle
Bishakha Subedi
Natasa Subotin
Justus von Süsskind
Yuri Sugiura
Steffi Suhr
Laurin Sulz
Luzia Sulz
Rebekka Sulz
Brigitte Surberg
Annette Süßer
Beatrice Swiatkowski
Kerstin Syring-Krück
Nikola Szafran

T

Inge Tacke
Tagesstätte für psychisch kranke Menschen
Tamara
Sigrid Tannert
Sena Tasli
Antonietta Tassone
Rosa Tassone
Tatyana
Renate Taube
Tauchclub Amphiprion Sindelfingen e.V.
Pita Taulien
Johanna Täusch
Ursula Tauscher
Irmtraud Tautz
Lucy Tawn
Katja Tegler
Annemarie Teich
Elke Teich
Regina Teichmann
Sabine Tenambergen
Sara Terhorst
Elvira Teske
Anka Thalmann
Antje Thaux
Christiane Theilmann
Monika Theilmann
Ulrike Theiss
Diane Thelen
Petra Thelen
Helga Thiel
Jule Louise Thiel
Ines Thiel-Müller
Lucas Thiering
Heidrun Thiery
Helga Thomann
Regina Thomann
Margaretha Thomas
Andrea Thon
Sigrid Thumfart

Petra Thums
Anke Thurack
Judith Thurner
Susanne Thyringer
Emily Tiedtke
Elfie Tinu
Heike Tirpitz
Estella Tischer
Helma Tita-Lindemann
Eva Tittel
Lisa Tobie
Rachel Toews
Christel Tofaute
Elke Tondera
Marion Tondera
Sissy Tongendorff
Melissa Topcic
Dagmar Torres Reyes
Yaren Su Tosun
Barbara Toth
Claire Trage
Jennifer Trageser
Sylvia Tratner
Claudia Traub
Martina Traub
Marie Johanna Trautmann
Andrea Trautnitz
Petra Tremmel
Andrea Trempel
Margareta Trenz
Theresa Treuer
Jasmine Trinh
Tanja Trojan
Maria Tröndle
Tanja Troppenz
Annette Trösken
Ingeborg Tröster
Katja Trumpold
Rosa Maria Trunk
Sohie Tscharntke
Claudia Tschirner
Esther Tschudi
Ildikó Tumbass
Leo Tunc
Mia Tunc
Turnseehort, Kinder und Erzieherinnen
Maya Tworek
Tamara Tziroulnikoff

U

Ricarda Uerlings
Elke Uhlig
Kilian Uhlig
Amelia Ulanowicz
Susan Ulbricht
Maximilian Ullmer
Beate Ulrich
Heidrun Ultes-Nitsche
Michelle Underberg
Regina Ungeheuer
Jana Unmüssig
Lydia Unmüßig
Katharina Unruh
Gabriele Urschel
Kimberley Urselmann
Beysa Uysal

V

Gabriele Vaillant
Valentin
Ute Vanselow
Gabi Vasen
Britta Vasta
Katrin Vastarg
Hanna Vayhinger
Sigrid Vedovelli
Gudrun Veiel
Brigitte Veit
K. Veit-Potzki
Zhorzh Velikov
Constanze Velimvassakis
Simone Velten
Gaia Venturino
Verein Arlesheim Kreativ
Ruth Verfürden
Lara Verschragen
Jutta Verstege

Enza Verzi
Hanne Vetter
Susanne Vetter
Ilonka Vidmar
Anna-Maria Viehöfer
Viktoria
Andrea Vildosola
Natalia Vlachou
Katrin Vogel
Sabine Vogelpoth
Beate Vögler
Martina Vogt
Monika Vohrer
Ilse Voigt
Katja Voland
Sabine Volbert
Frederic Völkel
Ronja Volkmer
Barbara Vollath-Sommer
Dorit Vollmer
Sabine Vollmer
Verena Volonté Baer
Beate Volz
Elke Volz
Uta Volz
Florian Vonnahme
Andrea Vössing
Gisela de Vries

W

Doris Waage
Ruth Wabschke
Claudia Wachendorfer
Annette Wachter
Annette Wackershauser
Jessica Wagemann
Birgit Wagner
Gaby Wagner
Isabel Wagner
Jessika Wagner
Karin Wagner
Renate Wagner
Sabine Wagner
Ursula Wagner
Helke Wahl
Gabrielle Waigand
Monika Waigel
Sundos Wais
Christian Wald
Isabell Wald
Sabine Wald
Waldorfschule Frankenthal, Klasse 7
Waldorfschule St. Georgen
Monika Wallenwein
Ben Wallinowski
Renate Wallner
Anne de Walmont
Tina Waltenberger
Beate Walter
Christa Walter
Doris Walter
Katharina Walter
Maja Walter
Matthias Walter
René Walter
Sabine Walter
Sina Walter
A. Walther
Susanne Walz
Gisela Wandres
Christiane Warmuth
Karin Warnecke
Pia Warnecke
Elisabeth Wass
Susanne Wassmann
Angela Wassmer
Konrad Waßmer
Gertrud Wass-Moschina
Lilli Wawrzynek
Angelika Weber
Eva Weber
Lucie Weber
Marion Weber
Paul Weber
Regina Weber
Simone Weber
Sonja Weber

Susanna Weber
Susanne Weber
Wally Weber
Ulrike Weber-Berger
Elke Webster
Inge Wedekind
Amelie Jessica Wegener
Catrin Wegener
Semih Wegmann
Doris Wegner
Dana Wehner
Monika Wehrstein
Doreen Weichert
Lilly Sophie Weichert
Rebecca Weick
Gabi Weidlandt
Dietlind Weidmann
Andrea Weidner
Dagmar Weigel
Maren Weil
Bianca Weiler
Birgit Weindl
Christa Weingärtner
Evelyn Weinl
Barbara Weis
Ilona Weis
Magnus Weis
Christina Weisbrod
Mechthild Weisbrod
Monica Weisheit
Andrea Weiß
Annette Weiß
Annkathrin Weiß
Catarina Weiß
Eva Weiß
Iris Weiß
Irmhild Weiß
Isolde Weiß
Jutta Weiß
Katharina Weiß
Petra Weiß
Uli Weiß
Birgit Weißbach
Melanie Weißenfeld
Marion Weitzsäcker
Volker Wellhäußer
Anke Wellner-Kempf
Claudia Welsch
Claudia Welteke
Gisi Wende
Anna Wenger
Birgit Wenzel
Ingrid Wenzel
Maria Wenzel
Monika Weppelmann
Heidi Werkmann
Werkstätten Materialhof, Turmgruppe
Sonja Werle
Robbie Wernecke
Sonja Wernecke
Andrea Werner
Marina Werner
Christine Wertheim
Margaret Wertheim
Jana Wessel-Bothe
Katharina Wessel-Bothe
Saskia Wessel-Bothe
Verene Westermann
Mildred Westerworth
Marina Westkamp
Heidrun Westkemper
Rosemarie Wetzel
Brigitte Wichlei-Spiegel
Sarina Wichmann
Christina Widmann
Corina Widmann
Katrin Wiech
Elke Wieczorek
Gerlinde Wiedenmann
Karin Wiedemann
Antje Wiedmann
Esther Wiedmann
Jule Wiegele
Angelika Wiegert
Mechthild Wiehe
Petra Wieland
Kerstin Wienen

Jona Jakob Wiens
Karin Wierschin
Karin Wiesbach
Nicole Wiesenhöfer
Gabriela Wiesmann
Isabelle Wiessler
Anke Wiest
Andrea Wild
Kerstin Wild
Petra Wild
Erika Wilhelms
Helga Wilke
Silvia Wilke
Karin Wilker
Bettina Will
Claudia Will
Doris Wille
Petra Wille
Sigrid Willer
Beate Willing
Silke von Willigen
Denis Willinger
Helga Winckler
Dagmar Windthorst
Gabriela Winkler
Sigrid Winkler
Susanne Winkler
Ulrike Winkler
Juliana Madeleine Winter
Mareike Winter
Petra Winter
Anna Winterhalder
Jutta Winterling
Elke Winterscheid
Heike Wipfler
Maja Wiprächtiger
Anja Wirth
Corinna Wirth
Ruth Wisler
Doris Wisniewski
Heike Withelm-Huber
Klaudia Witkowska
Stephanie Wittenberg
Renate Eva Maria Wittich
Helga Wittig
Monika Wittlinger
Gabriele Wittlinger de González
Susanne Wittner
Martina Wittwer
Nina Witzenrath
Karin Wloka
Kristina Wockenfuß
Elke Wodrich
Ella Wohlgezogen
Jenny Wohlhüter
Dorothea Wohlleber
Andrea Wöhrle
Caroline Wolf
Corina Wolf
Friederika Wolf
Gabi Wolf
Gundrun Wolf
Heidi Wolf
Kerstin Wolf
Magdalena Wolf
Marion Wolf
Petra Wolf
Ursula Wolf
Sigrid Wolff
Waltraud Wolff
Sibylle Wolfgramm
Silke Wolf-Hütten
Mieke Wolkenar
Wollewerkstatt Rommelsbach
Nina Wöllgens
Carla Linn Wolsiffer
Sigrid Wolter
Roswitha Worm
Agnes Wörner
Martina Wörner
Monika Wörner
Leonie Wsewolodski
Kathrin Wucherer
Margret Wulf-Freitag
Filomena Wunderlich
Hilde Wunsch

Madlen Wursthorn
Leopold Wuttig
Nepomuk Wuttig
Bettina Wyderka

X

Xia Mi
Wenzhe Xia

Y

Ke Xin Yan
Daria Yersin
Güney Yilmaz
Ela Yüksel
Zeysan Yurdakul

Z

Karin Zahn-Aigner
Angela Zähringer
Janina Zähringer-Coronel
Judith Zähringer-Krebietke
Petra Zai-Englert
Karen Zander-Haist
Barbara Zanger
Dörte Zbikowski
Verena Zbikowski
Danijela Zebic
Maximilian Zeh
Isabell Zehnbauer
Sabine Zeidler
Petra Zeil
Andreas Zein
Bettina Zelle
Franka Zellerer
Ulla Zellmann-Seyfferth
Dominic Zelmer
Luzia Zerr
Kristin Zessin
Susanne Zetzmann
Michelle Zeuner-Mayer
Rhena Zibold
Kerstin Ziegle
Christine Ziegler
Elias Ziegler
Irmgard Ziegler
Lynn Ziegler
Theresa Ziegler
Ute Ziegler
Veronika Ziegler
Inge Ziehmann
Andrea Zielinski
Katharina Ziemainz
Hella Ziese
Dorothea Zimmer
Angelika Zimmermann
Axel Zimmermann
Beate Zimmermann
Birgit Zimmermann
Carmen Zimmermann
Heidrun Zimmermann
Elli Zink
Petra Zinnitz
Christine Anita Zipfel
Madlen Zipfel
Ute Zirrgiebel
Margot Zöger
Martina Zöller
Iris Zöllner
Heidi Zorn
Sabine Zotter
Britta Zubrod-Nikisch
Karin Zugck
Barbara Zünd
Silvia Zund
Ute Zundel
Sylvia Zürker
Sonja Zustra

Compilation of Exhibited Works

Judith Irrgang

Christine Wertheim, Margaret Wertheim, and the Institute For Figuring

Coral Forest—Nin Imma, 2007–14
Crocheted plastic, SonoTube, and chicken wire
ca. 62 × 54 × 35 in. / 157 × 137.2 × 89 cm

Coral Forest—Next Generation, 2007–21
Crocheted videotape and plastic, Sonotube, and chicken wire
ca. 48 × 45 × 42 in. / 121.9 × 114.3 × 106.7 cm

Coral Forest—Little Orange Follower, 2008–21
Crocheted plastic bags by Siew Chu Kerk,
with armature wire, yarn, and steel
ca. 29 × 15 × 15 in. / 74 × 40 × 40 cm

Coral Forest—Eryali, 2007–21
Crocheted yarn, SonoTube, and chicken wire
ca. 51 × 48 × 43 in. / 129.5 × 121.9 × 109.2 cm

Coral Forest—Medusa, 2007–14
Crocheted yarn, SonoTube, and chicken wire
ca. 63 × 39 × 29 in. / 160 × 99 × 73.7 cm

Coral Forest—Stheno, 2007–16
Crocheted yarn, SonoTube, and chicken wire
Jorian Polis Schutz Collection
ca. 64 × 33 × 31 in. / 162.6 × 83.6 × 78.8 cm

Branched Anemone Garden
Crocheted yarn, felt, baskets, and sand
Lisa Yun Lee Collection
ca. 96 × 22 × 20 in. / 243.8 × 55.9 × 50.8 cm

Bleached Reef
Crocheted yarn, felt, baskets, wire, and sand
ca. 94 × 29 × 24 in. / 238.8 × 73.7 × 61 cm

Toxic Reef—CO$_2$CA CO$_2$LA Ocean
Crocheted yarn and videotape, with ring-pull tops,
glitter, sequins, tinsel, plastic diamonds,
bridal adornments, medical waste, and sand
ca. 94 × 29 × 24 in. / 238.8 × 73.7 × 61 cm

A set of six large totemic sculptures, standing on pedestals. Three of the *Coral Forests* are crocheted from yarn, and three from plastic. Where the yarn works reference the organic beauty of nature, the plastic pieces refer to our petrochemical age and the postmodern presence of synthetics. It incorporates coral pieces by Evelyn Hardin, Sarah Simons, Anitra Menning, Anna Mayer, Christina Simons, Jemima Wyman, Clare O'Callaghan, Shari Porter, Heather McCarren, Jing Wong, Gina Cacciolo, Helen Bernasconi, Marianne Middelberg, Helle Jorgensen, Barbara Wertheim, Katherine Wertheim, Una Morrison, Beverly Griffiths, Jane Canby, Tane Clarke, Nancy Yahrous, Kathleen Greco, Pate Conaway, Matt Adnam, Suha Mulqui, and Siew Chu Kerk, and pieces from the *Baden-Baden Satellite Reef*.

Branched Anemone Garden is one of the first reefs the Wertheim sisters crocheted. During its life the piece has undergone various "evolutionary" phases, leading to its current incarnation in the round. The work was inspired by the Great Barrier Reef and and by the color palette of the mountain ranges in Central Austalia. It incorporates coral pieces by Helen Bernasconi, Shari Porter, Sarah Simons, Lynn Latta, and David Orozco, and pieces from the *Baden-Baden Satellite Reef*.

The *Bleached Reef* is an invocation of coral "bleaching," the phenomena living reefs undergo in response to stresses such as pollution and warming waters. In exhibition settings, the *Bleached Reef* is usually paired as a diptych with the *Toxic Reef,* a black-and-white tableau crocheted from yarn, plastic, and videotape. It incorporates coral pieces by Marianne Middelberg, Nancy Lewis, Nadia Severns, Evelyn Hardin, Sarah Simons, Arlene Mintzer, Dagma Frinta, Jill Schreier, Pamela Stiles, Irene Lundgaard, Una Morrison, Barbara Van Elsen, Christina Simons, Anna Mayer, Helle Jorgensen, and Vonda N. McIntyre as well as pieces by vintage doily makers and unknown Chinese factory workers.

Hyperbolic Sea Snake
By Helen Bernasconi
Crocheted hund-spun, hand-dyed yarn
Origin: Bonnie Doon, Australia
ca. 240 × 15 × 15 in. / 609.6 × 38.1 × 38.1 cm

Carnation Mound
By Marianne Middelberg with tails by Sarah Simons
Crocheted yarn and basket
ca. 40 × 20 × 6 in. / 101.6 × 50.8 × 15.3 cm

Latvian Pod
From the *Latvian Satellite Reef*, curated by Tija Viksna
Crocheted yarn and garden wire
ca. 30 × 20 × 15 in. / 76.2 × 50.8 × 38.1 cm

The *Mathematics Blackboard* is a drawing created on site on an old-style school blackboard, which diagrams the mathematics of hyperbolic geometry underlying the forms of living and crocheted reef organisms.

Mathematics Blackboard, 2022
School blackboard paint and chalk
Drawing created on site by Margaret Wertheim
48 × 192 in. / 122 × 488 cm

Pod Worlds

A series of small vitrined *Pod Worlds*, each invoking a miniature coral universe. These works contain complex and delicate pieces by some of the *Crochet Coral Reef* project's most skilled and beloved crafters. Some of the *Pods* are crocheted in yarn; others are made from beaded pieces resembling small Byzantine gems. Several are made from plastic, and these works sit on a bed of "plastic sand" harvested from the Great Pacific Garbage Patch. One *Pod* is crocheted from electroluminescent wire, designed for military applications such as lighting the insides of tanks.

Pod World—Red and White (2006–21)
Beads, thread, circuit-board wire, anodized wire, sand, and rocks.
Corals by Anita Bruce, Lucia LaVilla-Havelin, and Sarah Simons

Pod World—Wire and Beaded (2009–21)
Beads, thread, circuit-board wire, anodized wire, sand, and rocks.
Corals by Vonda N. McIntyre, Anita Bruce, and unknown Irish reefer

Pod World—Wire and Beaded II (2009–21)
Beads, thread, anodized wire, sand, and rocks.
Corals by Sarah Simons and unknown Chicago reefer

Pod World—Beaded Baroque (2009–21)
Beads, thread, wire, hair scrunchie, sand, and rocks.
Corals by Vonda N. McIntyre, Sue Von Ohlsen, Rebecca Peapples, and Diana Simons

Pod World—Beaded Baroque II (2009–21)
Beads, thread, wire, plastic bottle, sand, and rocks.
Corals by Sue Von Ohlsen, Rebecca Peapples, and Nadia Severns

Pod World—Hyperbolic (2006–19)
Yarn, mercerized cotton, Victorian glass, wire, sand, rocks.
Corals by Anitra Menning, Heather McCarren, Margaret Wertheim, and Christine Wertheim

Pod World—Plastic Fantastic (2008–21)
Plastic bottles, yarn, and plastic debris gathered from the Great Pacific Garbage Patch on Kamilo Beach, Hawaii.
Corals by Nadia Severns and Christine Wertheim (with Noah Purifoy)

Pod World—Plastic Fantastic Too (2006–16)
Jelly Yarn, plastic bags, and plastic debris gathered from the
Great Pacific Garbage Patch on Kamilo Beach, Hawaii.
Corals by Christine Wertheim and Kathleen Greco

Pod World—Eye Jellies (2009–21)
Plastic bin-liner bags, lubricant eye drop vials used by the artist,
wire, sand, and rocks. Jellyfish by Margaret Wertheim and
Christine Wertheim

Pod World—Cambrian Explosion (2006–21)
Yarn, handspun yarn, cable ties, wire, sand, rocks.
Corals by Evelyn Hardin, Christine Wertheim, and Helen Bernasconi

Pod World—Staghorn Garden (2009)
Mercerized thread, batting, biscuit tin, super-magnets,
and sand. Corals by Mieko Fukuhara

Pod World—EL Wire (2006–19)
Military-grade, Israeli-made electroluminescent wire, power adapters,
sand, and rocks. Corals by Eleanor Kent and Margaret Wertheim

Each vitrined work is 40 × 40 × 40 cm / 15¾ × 15¾ × 15¾ in.

Holy Documents

18 framed objects, including personal letters, notes, stickers, etc. from
people who sent the Wertheims contributions for the *Crochet Coral Reef*
Framed dimensions: each 20 × 24.5 cm

HD-A   Drawing of crochet reef sculpture by Kathleen Greco
HD-B   "Made in China" labels from bridal adornments
HD-C   Letter from Mieko Fukuhara
HD-D   Letter and label with safety pins from Evelyn Hardin
HD-E   Postcards from feminist sci-fi writer Vonda N. McIntyre
HD-F   Reef sculpture drawing by Christine Wertheim
HD-G   Name tags from *Crochet Coral Reef* community contributors
HD-H   Labels from yarns used by Margaret and Christine in the *Crochet Coral
        Reef* project
HD-I   Letter from Alicia Escott about reef drawings done on plastic trash
HD-J   Envelopes containing tatted letters for the sampler artwork, commissioned
        by the Wertheim sisters from Russian crafter Anna Blinohvatova
HD-K   Taxonomy of plastic JellyYarn corals by Kathleen Greco
HD-L   Layout diagram of crocheted coral subreef by the sisters' mother,
        Barbara Wertheim
HD-M   *Kyoto News* press clipping, plus letter from the editor
HD-N   Postcards of knitted wire sea creatures by Anita Bruce
HD-O   Letter from Shari Porter about the Holy Spirit revealing hyperbolic crochet to her
HD-P   Crochet Reef label for *Reeficus Madness*, a large hanging subreef, by the
        mysterious Dr. Axt
HD-Q   Handwritten box lid from Evelyn Hardin with first revelations about
        this most remarkable contributor
HD   Small sampler, hand-tatted letters on hand-embroidered runner,
        made especially for the show at the Museum Frieder Burda

Each object is a letter, diagram, or note sent to the artists by a crochet reef contributor who explains their work or describes how they think it should be shown. Some are labels from their yarns or name tags attached to their pieces. Emotional, touching, and visually fascinating, this is a collection of personal memorabilia from some of the Reef project's most intimate contributors.

Evelyn Hardin and Friends, 2021
Tatted and embroidered linen
34 × 65 in. / 86.4 × 165 cm

This large-scale fabric work is modeled after samplers women used to make as they learned to embroider. The letters were hand-tatted by a Russian crafter the artists found on Etsy and commissioned to create letters, spelling out the names of the Reef project's most committed contributors. A hugely time-consuming labor of female craft skill, the piece was also inspired by the Wertheim's history growing up sewing their own clothes. Getting the letters "typeset" was a challenge; the aesthetic is reminiscent of medieval manuscripts. The title *Evelyn Hardin and Friends* honors Reef contributor Evelyn Hardin, "a brilliant force of creativity until her sudden death from cancer in 2014." Her personal story is often used by the artists as a tale about the undervaluing of women's creative powers. The letters were stitched on by Laura Im and Eileen van Schaik.

Red Nudibranch Reef, 2021
"Nudibranch" in traditional Japanese shiburi technique, with crocheted yarn, electrical capacitors, rocks and sand
ca. 35 × 19 × 15 in. / 88.9 × 48.3 × 38.1 cm

Green Nudibranch Reef
"Nudibranch" in traditional Japanese shiburi technique, with crocheted yarn, electrical capacitors, rocks, and sand
ca. 27 × 19 × 15 in. / 68.6 × 48.3 × 38.1 cm

Both works are centered around "nudibranchs"— scarves made from the traditional Japanese fabric technique of *shiburi*, which the artists discovered in a Venice store. Their use of found objects within the Reef project continues the theme of repurposing textile arts. The aesthetic is modeled on nineteenth-century natural history museum displays crossed with Hieronymus Bosch, purposefully mixing disparate elements including electronic circuit board capacitors. Again, the artists have incorporated toxic discarded objects, making a striking contrast with the crochet.

The Midden—The BAD Rubbish, 2021–22
Fishing net filled with plastic waste from the Museum Frieder Burda, including the plastic waste produced at home by all museum employees during a period of about four months.

This was how long it took to produce the *Baden-Baden Satellite Reef*, make all technical preparations, and install the exhibition. The *BAD Rubbish* project is modeled after the Wertheim's *Midden*, a project in which they kept all their domestic plastic trash for four years, from January 2007 to April 2011.

Baden-Baden Satellite Reef, 2021–22
In conjunction with the exhibition *Value and Transformation of Corals*, at the Museum Frieder Burda, Baden-Baden, from January 29 to June 26, 2022, the museum hosted the construction of a local *Satellite Reef*. Over four thousand people across Germany and a dozen other countries contributed more than forty thousand individual coral pieces to this installation, making it by far the largest *Satellite Reef* to date.

Baden-Baden Satellite Reef consists of six individual, freestanding coral islands that were given the following titles by the artists:

Baden-Baden Satellite Reef: Variegated
Baden-Baden Satellite Reef: Neon
Baden-Baden Satellite Reef: The Deep
Baden-Baden Satellite Reef: Spotted
Baden-Baden Satellite Reef: Tricolor
Baden-Baden Satellite Reef: Toxic

The *Baden-Baden Satellite Reef* was created over a period of three months in late 2021 and early 2022, following a general aesthetic scheme designed by Margaret and Christine Wertheim. With curatorial guidance from Christine, a series of six large-scale sculptural coral "islands," plus a collection of wall-mounted coral "paintings," were assembled from the vast mass of submitted corals pieces.
The artistic team from the workshop of the Museum Frieder Burda worked intensively on this collective project for many months to produce the largest *Satellite Reef* ever created.
Special thanks are due to Kathrin Dorfner, the head of the museum's workshop who served as chief reef coordinator; and to Christina Humpert and Martina Schulz for overseeing the curatorial configuration of the reef, assisted by the superb crochet-on-demand skills of Charlotte Reiter, Susan Reiss, Silke Habich, and Paula Hirth, who were all essential for bringing this project to fruition.

Foyer wall, ground floor:
Wall Work: Five Fathoms Deep

The wide range of corals that were submitted for the *Baden-Baden Satellite Reef* made it possible to create other unique coral paintings that, like the reef itself, were created and passionately adapted for the exhibition in the Museum Frieder Burda by Kathrin Dorfner and her team from the museum workshop.

Mezzanine:
Impressions of a SeaScape I–V

Large hall, ground floor:
Baden-Baden Coral Frieze

Coral panels on the museum elevator over four floors:
Corals Ascending I–VIII

Historical Materials

Crochet Magazines

Star Book no. 59, 1948
"Ruffled Doilies and the Pansy Doily"
American Thread Company, Inc., 1948
10 1/2 × 7 1/2 in. / 26.7 × 19 cm

Clark's J. & P. Coats Crochet Pattern
Book no. 253, 1949
"Ruffled Doilies"
Spool Cotton Company, 1949
10 5/8 × 7 5/8 in. / 27 × 19.3 cm

Coats & Clark's Crochet Pattern
Book no. 327, 1957
"Ruffled Doilies"
Coats & Clark Inc., 1957
10 1/2 × 7 5/7 in. / 27 × 19.4 cm

Four Books

Flora Klickmann, *The Home Art Series: Artistic Crochet*, 1914
Published by *The Girl's Own Paper and Woman's Magazine*, London
Third edition, 114 pages
Containing novel beadings, insertions, and edgings suitable for underwear and dress trimmings, exquisite floral designs in Irish crochet. Also practical suggestions both simple and advanced, for tea cloths and bedspreads
9 × 6 in. / 22.9 × 15.3 cm

Thérèse de Dillmont, *La Dentelle Ténériffe*, Bibliothèque DMC, Mulhouse (Alsace), Dollfus-Mieg & Cie, Mulhouse, Belfort, Paris, ca. 1930
5 1/2 × 8 in. / 14 × 20.3 cm

Diatom Book, created by Sarah Simons, 2008
Handmade, hand-bound flip book of traditional doily patterns
3 × 3 in. / 7.5 × 7.5 cm

Doilies

Various vintage lace doilies from the Wertheim's private collection, plus several from the collection of Roxanne Steinberg
Various diameters: 4 3/4 to 7 in. / 12 to 18 cm

One red tatted doily by *Föhr Satellite* reefer
Gertrud von Krichau-Anderssen
Diameter: ca. 6 in. / 15.5 cm

Various plastic doilies, 1960s
Various diameters: 6 to 12 3/4 in. / 15 to 32.5 cm

Leopold and Rudolf Blaschka

Glass model of a precious coral (Corallium rubrum), undated
Two parts, base: 1/2–2 3/8 × 6 1/4 × 4 1/4 in. / 1–6 cm × 16 × 11 cm
Museum für Naturkunde Berlin

Glass model of a cushion coral (Cladocora caespitosa), undated
Two parts, 2 3/8 × 4 1/2 in. / 6 × 11.5 cm and individual model:
1 1/4 × 1 1/8 in. / 3 × 2.8 cm
Museum für Naturkunde Berlin

Glass models of a common jellyfish (Aurelia aurita), undated
Eight parts, overall: 1/4–1 5/8 × 7 7/8 × 6 3/4 in. / 0.5–4 × 20 × 17 cm
Museum für Naturkunde Berlin

Original coral colony with inlaid glass models of polyp heads, original size, alongside an enlarged model of a single polyp. These stony corals, which are native to the Mediterranean, can cover areas of more than one hundred square meters.

Ernst Haeckel

Kunstformen der Natur (Art Forms in Nature), 1904
Verlag des Bibliographischen Instituts, Leipzig and Vienna, 1904
First edition with one hundred illustrations and descriptive text, general explanation, and a systematic overview
Each sheet 13 5/8 × 10 1/4 in. / 34.6 × 26 cm
Museum Frieder Burda, Baden-Baden

"Report on the Radiolaria Collected by H.M.S. Challenger during the Years 1873–1876, 1887," in *Report on the Scientific Results of the Voyage of H.M.S. Challenger during the Years 1873–1876*, Zoology, vol. 18, Edinburgh, 1887
12 1/2 × 10 1/4 × 7/8 in. / 31.9 × 25.8 × 2.2 cm
Senckenberg Naturmuseum Frankfurt

Radiolarien (Radolaria), 1915
Cover page of a portfolio bearing the dedication
"1834–1894 Seiner lieben Enkelin Else Meyer (Leipzig) zu ihrem
21. Geburtstage 22. September 1915 Mit besten Wünschen
Ihr 81jähriger Grossvater Ernst Haeckel (Jena)"
(1834–1894 to his dear granddaughter Else Meyer [Leipzig]
on her twenty-first birthday, September 22, 1915, with best wishes
from her eighty-one-year-old grandfather Ernst Haeckel [Jena])
Watercolor on paper
18 7/8 × 15 7/4 in. / 47.9 × 39 cm
Senckenberg Naturmuseum Frankfurt

Ohne Titel (Baum) (Untitled [Tree]), undated
Watercolor on paper
5 1/2 × 9 in. / 14 × 23 cm
Senckenberg Naturmuseum Frankfurt

Ohne Titel (Eisberg) (Untitled [Iceberg]), undated
Watercolor on paper
9 1/8 × 13 1/2 in. / 23.1 × 34,3 cm
Senckenberg Naturmuseum Frankfurt

The collection was published in installments between 1899 and 1904. In 1904 this first book edition was published with one hundred partially colored plates, each with a page of explanatory text including the numbering that corresponds to the species described. Many plates were produced using a combination of printing processes, including the combination of chromolithography, which had been rarely used before that time, and photographic reproductions.

Crochet Coral Reef →

Past Exhibitions and *Pod Worlds*

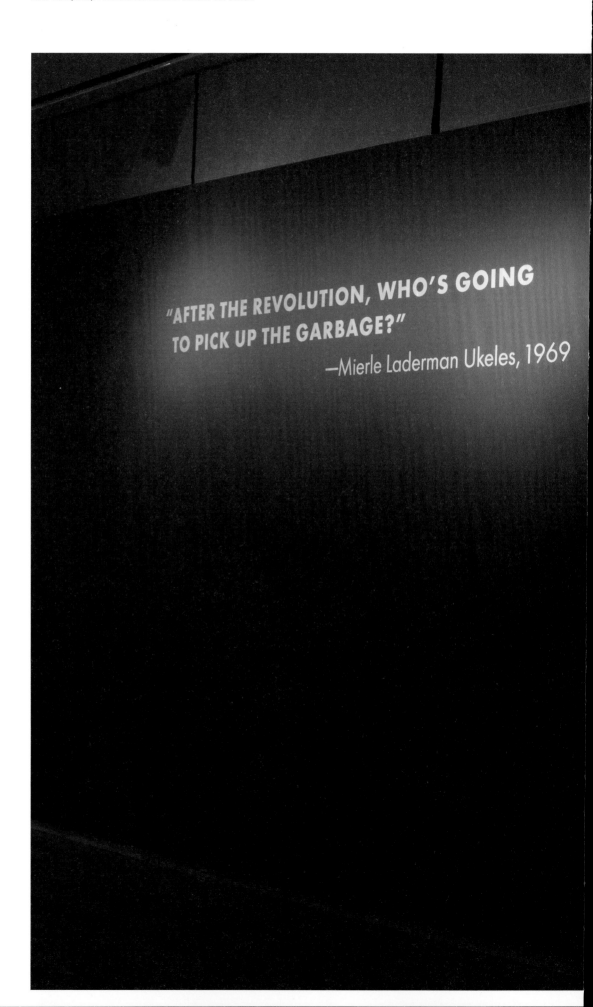

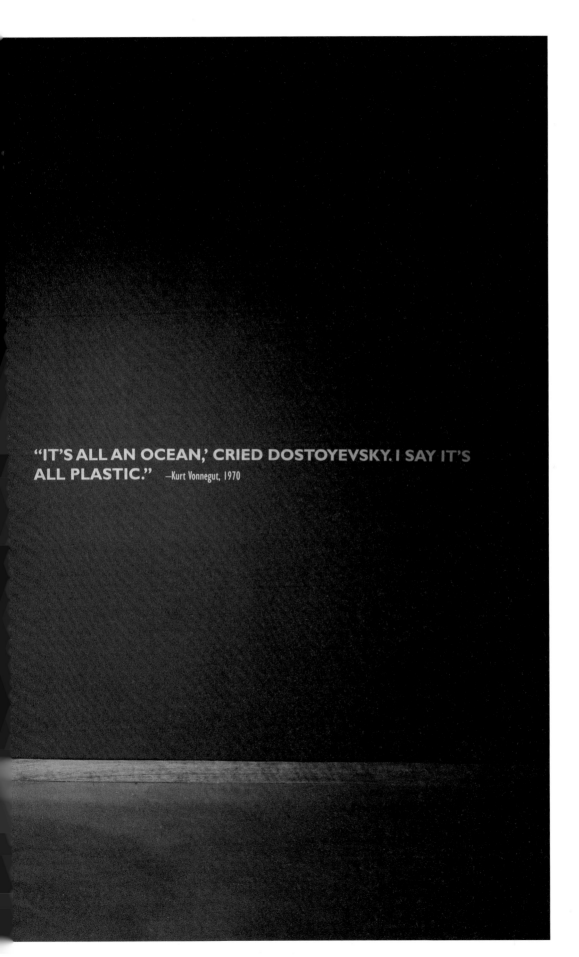

"IT'S ALL AN OCEAN,' CRIED DOSTOYEVSKY. I SAY IT'S ALL PLASTIC." —Kurt Vonnegut, 1970

Top: *Pod World—Staghorn Corals*, featuring
corals by Mieko Fukuhara, at the Museum of
Arts and Design in New York, 2016

Bottom: *Pod World—Plastic Fantastic Too*, featuring bottle
trees by Nadia Severns and plastic jellyfish by Vanessa Garcia,
at the Museum of Arts and Design in New York, 2016

Pages 194–195: *Bleached Reef* and *Toxic Reef* with the
Mathematics Blackboard at the 58th Venice Biennale, 2019 →

Toxic Reef at the National Museum of Natural History, Smithsonian Institution, Washington, DC, 2010. Featuring plastic corals by Christine Wertheim, Siew Chu Kerk, Evelyn Hardin, Clare O'Callaghan, and Sarah Simons

Knitted wire sea creature
by Anita Bruce

Top: Knitted wire sea creature
by Anita Bruce

Bottom: White coral spires by Evelyn Hardin, curated by
Ann Wertheim at Track 16 Gallery, Los Angeles, 2009

← *Reeficus Yellownicus* by the mysterious
Dr. Axt, at the Science Gallery, Dublin, 2010

Top: *Green Reef* at the Scottsdale
Civic Center Library, 2009

Bottom: Our very first crochet reef in 2006. Featuring
sea slug by Marianne Middelberg, anemones by Christine
Wertheim, and rubble corals by Margaret Wertheim

Beaded jellyfish
by Vonda N. McIntyre

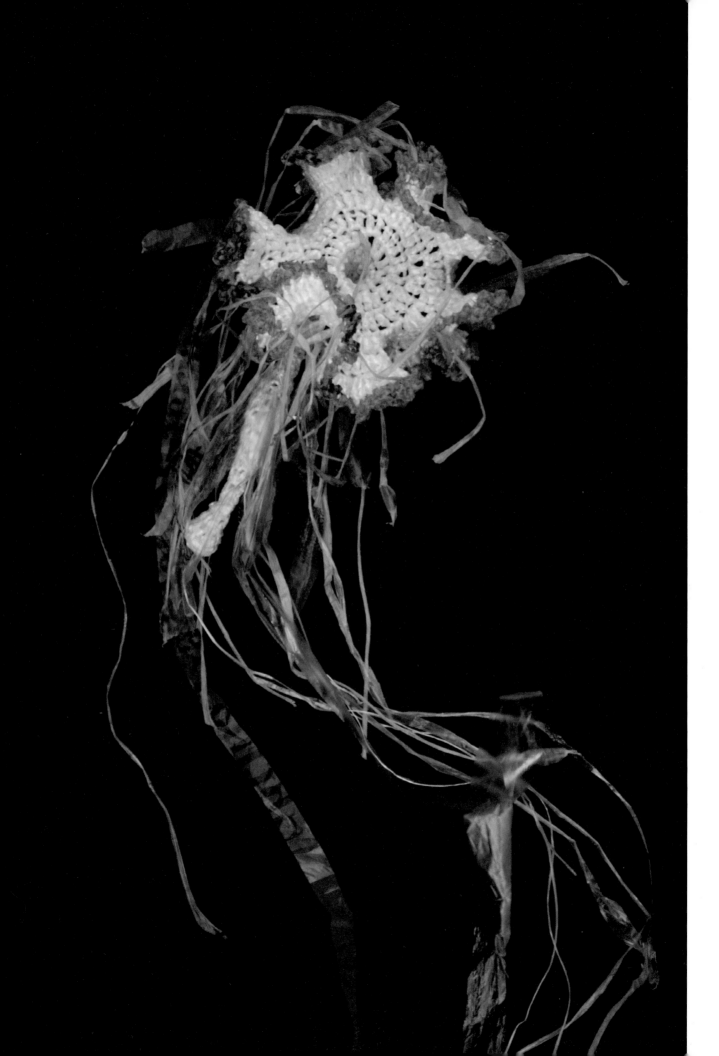

← Jellyfish crocheted from bin-liner bags by Margaret Wertheim

Anemone crocheted from *New York Times* wrappers, with drinking straw florets, by Clare O'Callaghan

Page 208: *Red Nudibranch Reef* by Christine and Margaret Wertheim, 2021

Page 209: *Green Nudibranch Reef* by Christine and Margaret Wertheim, 2021, featuring miniature coral pieces by unknown contributor from the *New York Satellite Reef*

Pages 210–211: *Pod World—Electroluminescent* featuring corals by Eleanor Kent and Margaret Wertheim, crocheted from military-grade EL wire, designed for lighting tanks

→

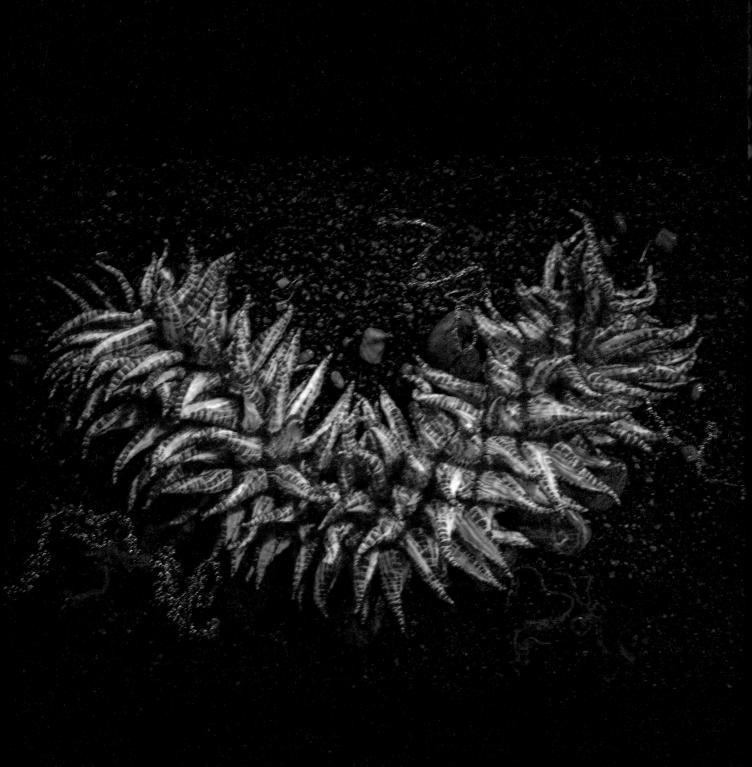

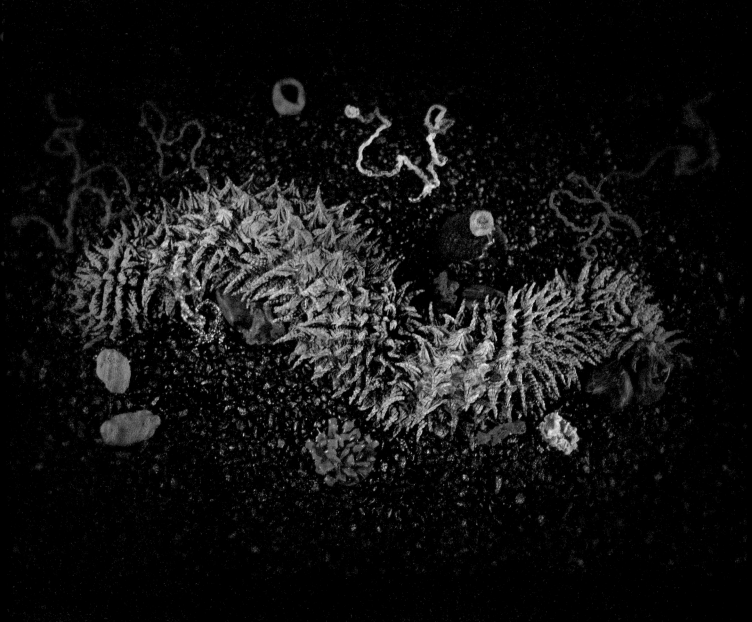

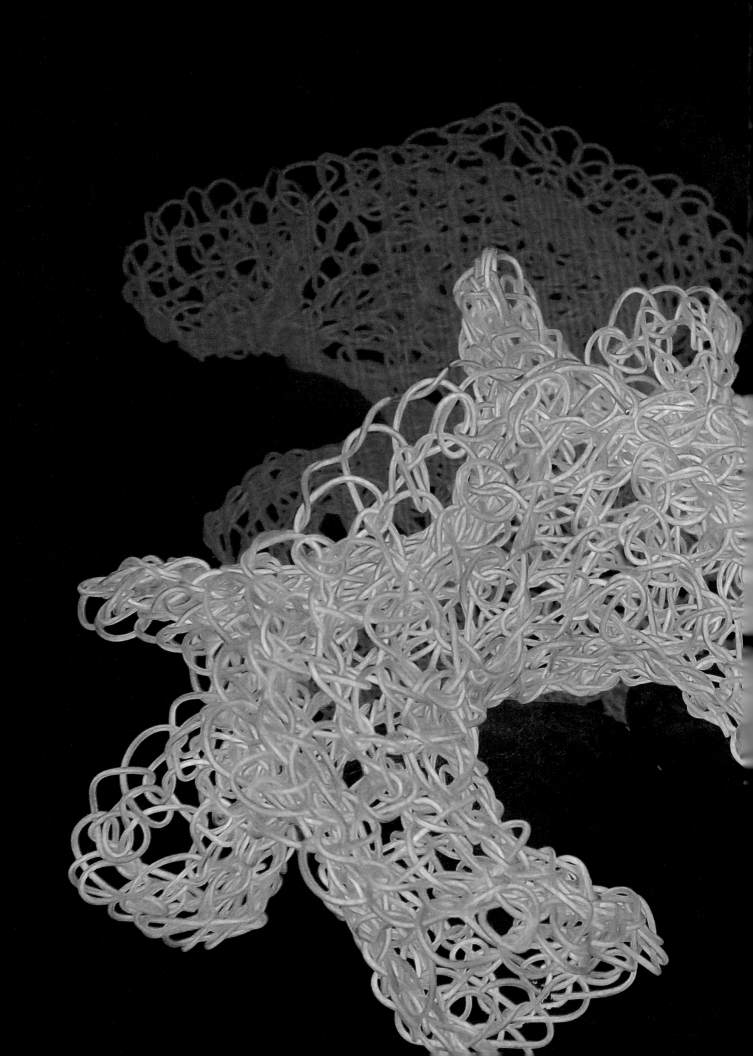

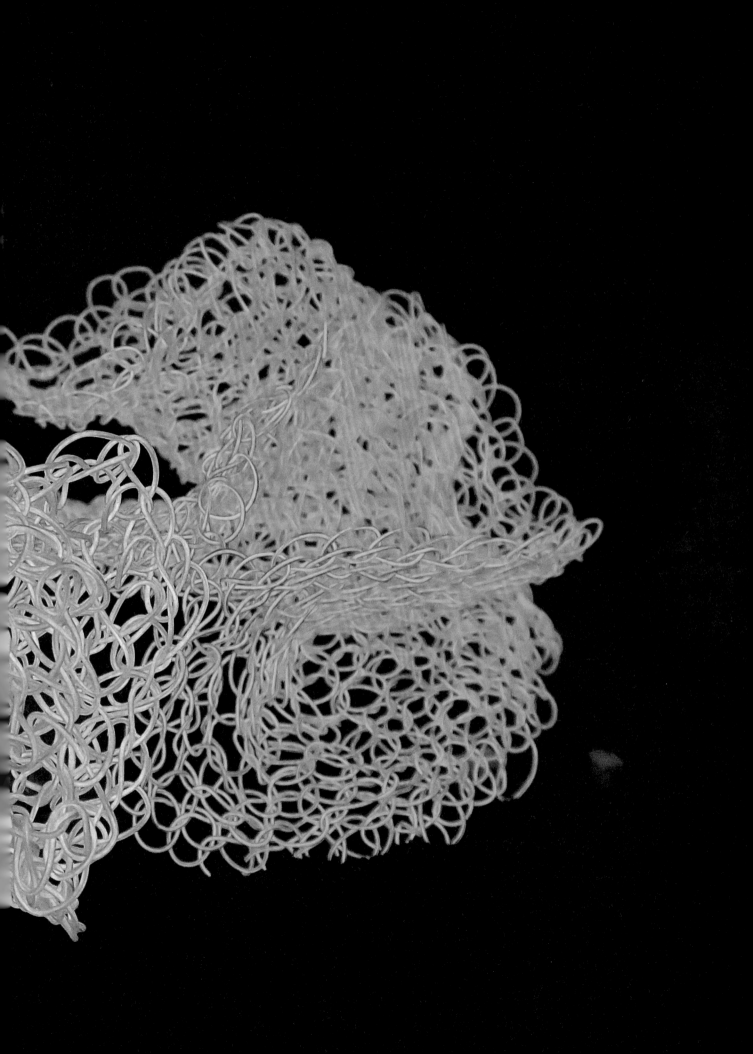

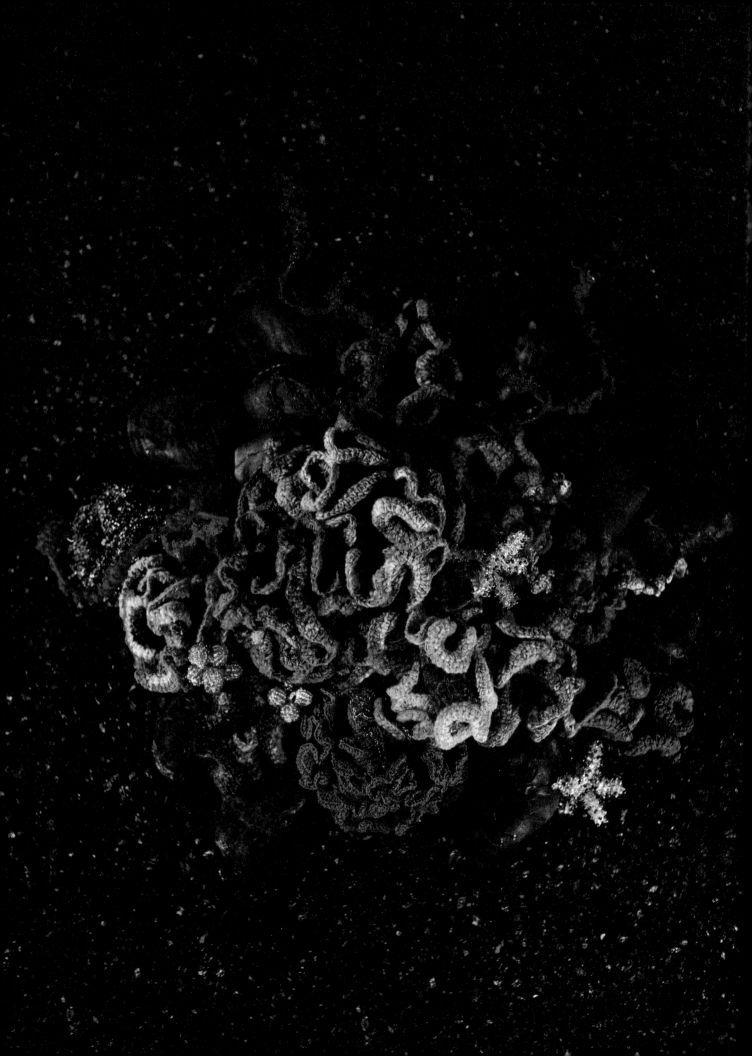

← *Pod World—Blue Coral Landscape* featuring Noru yarn corals by Irene Lundgaard and Orla Breslin, with spires by Christine Wertheim

Videotape and orange corals by Christine Wertheim. The video piece is crocheted from two VHS tapes of *The Matrix*, one from the United States and one from Russia

Page 214: *Pod World—Wire and Beaded*, featuring anodized wire coral by unknown Chicago reefer with miniature beaded sea creatures by Sarah Simons

Page 215: *Pod World—Red and White*, featuring pearl beaded anemone by Lucia LaVilla Haviland, and knitted wire sea creatures by Ania Bruce

→

Blue beaded coral by Sue Von Ohlsen.
Here the hyperbolic crochet algorithm is
translated into beaded peyote stitch.

→ Felted coral with cable-tie fronds by
Evelyn Hardin, mounted on wire-wrapped
stalk by Christine Wertheim

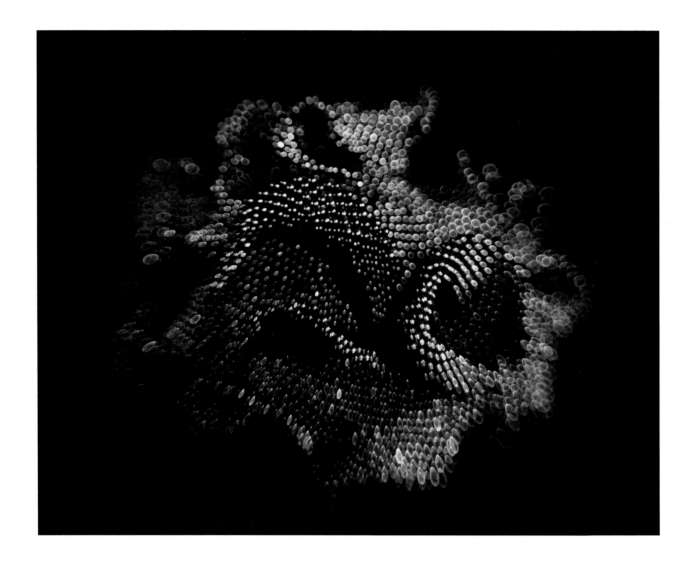

Pages 218–19:

1 → Jelly Yarn sea creature by Evelyn Hardin
2 → Carpet-yarn kelp by Margaret Wertheim
3 → Bubble anemone tower by Ildiko Szabo
4 → Octopus with hyperbolic tentacles by Helen Bernasconi
5 → Beaded Byzantine corals by Rebecca Peapples
6 → Plastic anemone crocheted from New York Times wrappers by Clare O'Callaghan
7 → Fingerling coral by Vonda N. McIntyre

8 → Fur-trimmed jellyfish by Ildiko Szabo
9 → Bin-liner plastic-bag jellyfish by Margaret Wertheim
10 → Knitted sea cucumber by Ildiko Szabo
11 → Fishing-line jellyfish by David Orozco
12 → Bubble coral by Jane Canby
13 → Jelly Yarn anemone inside snow globe by Katherine Greco
14 → Plastic sea creature with faux pearl boards by unknown UK reefer
15 → Pink spiral tube worms by Ildiko Szabo

Crochet Coral Reef—
Core Contributors

Evelyn Hardin (Dallas)
Anna Mayer (Los Angeles)
Jemima Wyman (Los Angeles)
Christina Simons (Los Angeles)
Sarah Simons (Los Angeles)
Clare O'Callaghan (Los Angeles)
Anitra Menning (Los Angeles)
Shari Porter (Los Angeles)
Helen Bernasconi (Australia)
Marianne Middelburg (Australia)
Barbara Wertheim (Australia)
Helle Jorgensen (Australia)
Ildiko Szabo (UK)
Anita Bruce (UK)
Una Morrison (Ireland)
Mieko Fukuhara (Japan)
Tija Viksna (Latvia)
Heather McCarren (CA)
Eleanor Kent (CA)
Dr. Axt (VT)
Nancy Lewis (VT)
Vonda N. McIntyre (WA)
Sue Von Ohlsen (PA)
Kathleen Greco (PA)
Rebecca Peapples (MI)
Nadia Severns (NY)
Arlene Mintzer (NY)
Jill Schrier (NY)
Pamela Stiles (NY)
Siew Chu Kerk (NY)
Dagmar Frinta (NY)
Barbara Van Elsen (NY)
Aviva Alter (IL)
Paté Conaway (IL)
Jane Canby (AZ)

With
Ann Wertheim
Elizabeth Wertheim
Katherine Wertheim
Gunta Jekabsone
Irene Lundgaard
Orla Breslin
Ashling Miller
Beverly Griffiths
Vanessa L. Garcia
David Orozco
Diana Simons
Allie Gerlach
Quoin

Catherine Chandler
Sally Giles
Kristine Brandel
Cindy Bennish
Spring Pace
Karen Frazer
Karen Page
Lynn Latta
Njoya Angrum
Gina Cacciolo
Chantal Hoareau
Myrna Gutierrez
Ying Wong
Lily M. Chin
Jessica Stapp
Kat Ramsland
Barbara Wakesfield
Amber Reyes
Barbara Robinson
Shirley Waxman
Ranu Mukherjee's class at CCA
Katy Bevan
Rosy Sykes
Jennifer White
Sharon Menges
Linda Shirey
Ellen Davis
Tane Clark
Nancy Youros
Ruth Carruthers
Aoife Canavan
Audrey Cremin
Elzbieta Rzechula
Emer Brady
Jacinta Douglass
Jennifer Byrne
Madge Kenny
Moira Jones
Serene Baird
Geraldine Coogan
Janice Ogata
Kate Bergh
Julie Tomiko Smith
Jen Hofer
Paula Peng
Theresa Bowen

And with the participation
of vintage doily makers and
unknown Chinese factory workers

Crochet Coral Reef—
Selected Exhibitions

Solo exhibitions are indicated by an asterisk;
entries without asterisks are group exhibitions.

2021	*Helsinki Biennial: The Same Sea*, Helsinki
2019	*May You Live in Interesting Times*, 58th Venice Biennale
2018	*TRADE MARKINGS: Frontier Imaginaries Ed. No. 5*, Van Abbemuseum, Eindhoven
2017	*Crochet Coral Reef: CO$_2$CA CO$_2$LA OCEAN*, Mary Porter Sesnon Art Gallery, University of California Santa Cruz*
2016	*Crochet Coral Reef: Toxic Seas*, Museum of Arts and Design, New York*
2015	*Leonardo da Vinci, the Codex Leicester and the Creative Mind*, Minneapolis Institute of Art, Minneapolis
2013	*SPUN: Adventures in Textiles*, Denver Museum of Art
2012	*The Hyperbolic Crochet Coral Reef*, Museum Kunst der Westküste, Föhr*
2011	*Hyperbolic: Reefs, Rubbish, and Reason*, Alyce de Roulet Williamson Gallery, Art Center College of Design, Pasadena*
2011	*The Hyperbolic Crochet Coral Reef*, National Museum of Natural History, Smithsonian Institution, Washington, DC*
2011	*National Design Triennial: Why Design Now?*, Cooper Hewitt Smithsonian Design Museum, New York
2010	*Hyperbolic Crochet Coral Reef*, Science Gallery, Dublin*
2009	*Hyperbolic Crochet Coral Reef*, Track 16 Gallery, Los Angeles*
2008	*Hyperbolic Crochet Coral Reef*, Hayward Gallery Project Room, London*
2007	*Hyperbolic Crochet Coral Reef*, Chicago Cultural Center, Chicago*
2006	*6 Billion Perps Held Hostage: Artists Address Global Warming*, Andy Warhol Museum, Pittsburgh

All *Satellite Reefs,*
2007–2022

2021–22   *Baden-Baden Satellite Reef*—Hosted by Museum Frieder Burda
(Baden-Baden, Germany)
North Carolina Satellite Reef—Hosted by the North Carolina Museum of Art
(Raleigh, NC, USA)
Saratoga Springs Satellite Reef—Hosted by the Frances Young Tang Teaching
Museum and Art Gallery, Skidmore College (Saratoga Springs, NY, USA)
Ontario Satellite Reef—Hosted by the Ontario Science Center (Toronto, ON, Canada)

2021   *Urbana-Champaign Satellite Reef*––Hosted by University of Illinois
Urbana-Champaign, School of Art and Design (Urbana-Champaign, IL, USA)
Mexico City Satellite Reef—Hosted by Red de Reproducción y Distribución
(Mexico City, Mexico)

2020–21   *Helsinki Satellite Reef*—Hosted by Helsinki Art Museum and the Helsinki Biennial
2021 (Helsinki, Finland)

2019   *Lehigh Satellite Reef*—Hosted by Lehigh University Art Galleries
(Bethlehem, PA, USA)

2018   *Eindhoven Satellite Reef*—hosted by Van Abbemuseum (Eindhoven, the Netherlands)
West Valley College Satellite Reef—Hosted by West Valley College
(Saratoga, CA, USA)

2016   *Del Rio Satellite Reef*—Hosted by Del Rio Council for the Arts (Del Rio, TX, USA)
UW La Crosse School Reef—Hosted by University of Wisconsin-La Crosse (WI, USA)
UC Santa Cruz Satellite Reef—Hosted by University of California Santa Cruz,
Institute of the Arts and Sciences (Santa Cruz, CA, USA)

2015   *San Antonio Satellite Reef*—Hosted by Southwest School of Art
(San Antonio, TX, USA)
Minneapolis Satellite Reef—Hosted by Minneapolis Institute of Art
(Minneapolis, MN, USA)

2014   *Zagreb Satellite Reef*—hosted by Ozana (Zagreb, Croatia)
Sunshine Coast Satellite Reef—Hosted by Caloundra Regional Gallery
(Caloundra, Queensland, Australia)
Methodist Ladies' College School Reef—Hosted by Methodist Ladies' College
(Melbourne, Australia)

2013   *Manchester Satellite Reef*—Hosted by Manchester Museum (Manchester, UK)
Baltimore Satellite Reef—Hosted by Gallery CA and Neighborhood Fiber Co.
(Baltimore, PA, USA)
Denver Satellite Reef—Hosted by the Denver Art Museum (Denver, CO, USA)
NYU Abu Dhabi Satellite Reef—Hosted by the New York University Abu Dhabi
Institute (Abu Dhabi, United Arab Emirates)

2012   *Föhr Satellite Reef*—Hosted by Museum Kunst der Westküste
(Föhr, Germany)
St. Petersburg Satellite Reef—Hosted by Florida Craftsman
(St. Petersburg, FL, USA)

Roanoke Valley Satellite Reef—Hosted by Roanoke College
(Roanoke, VA, USA)
Abbottsford School Reef—Hosted by the Abbotsford School
(Abbotsford, BC, Canada)

2011   *Asheville Satellite Reef*—Hosted by the Center for Craft Creativity and
Design (Ashville, NC, USA)
Lake Bonneville Satellite Reef—Hosted by Brolly Arts
(Lake Bonnevile, UT, USA)
Pennington School Reef—Hosted by the Pennington School
(Pennington, NJ, USA)
Maine Satellite Reef—Hosted by the West Oxford Agricultural Society
(Fryeburg, MN, USA)
Vassar College Reef—Hosted by Vassar College (Poughkeepsie, NY, USA)
RiAus Adelaide Satellite Reef—Hosted by the Royal Institution of
Australia (Adelaide, Australia)

2010   *Irish Satellite Reef*—Hosted by Science Gallery (Dublin, Ireland)
Cape Town Satellite Reef—Hosted by Woodstock Art Center
(Cape Town, South Africa)
Indianapolis Satellite Reef—Hosted by Indiana State Museum
(Indianapolis, IN, USA)
Gainesville, FL Satellite Reef—Hosted by University of Florida Library
(Gainesville, FL, USA)
Smithsonian Community Satellite Reef—Hosted by Smithsonian Institution,
National Museum of Natural History (Washington, DC, USA)
Melbourne Satellite Reef—Hosted by Burranja Gallery
(Melbourne, Australia)

2009   *Scottsdale Satellite Reef*—Hosted by Scottsdale Public Art
(Scottsdale, AZ, USA)
Scarsdale Middle School Reef—Hosted by Scarsdale Middle School
(Scarsdale, NY, USA)
Sydney Satellite Reef—Hosted by In Stitches art collective (Sydney, Australia)
Fukuoka Satellite Reef—Hosted by Museum Lab (Fukuoka, Japan)
Latvian Satellite Reef and *Latvian Schools Reef*—Hosted by Gallerie Consentio
(Riga, Latvia)

2008   *New York Satellite Reef*—Hosted by the New York Institute of the
Humanities, the New York Crochet Guild, and the Harlem Knitting Circle
(New York, NY, USA)
UK Satellite Reef—Hosted by Hayward Gallery at the Southbank Center
and the UK Crafts Council (London, England)
Gideon Hausner Jewish Day School Reef—Hosted by Gideon Hauser
Jewish Day School (San Jose, CA, USA)

2007   *Chicago Satellite Reef*—Hosted by the Jane Addams Hull-House Museum
and the Chicago Humanities Festival (Chicago, IL, USA)

Artist Biographies

Christine Wertheim,

cocreator of the *Crochet Coral Reef* project, is an artist and writer whose books include three poetic suites *The Book of Me*, *mUtter—bAbel*, and *+|'me'S-pace*. These fuse graphics and text to explore the potentialities of the English tongue, and relationships between infantile rage and global violence. Her poetry and critical writings on art, literature, and aesthetics have appeared in magazines such as *Cabinet*, *X-tra*, *n.paradoxa*, *BOMB*, *Entropy*, and *Jacket 2*. She has contributions in the recent anthologies *Cold War Cold World* and *Construction Sites for Possible Worlds*, both published by Urbanomic for MIT Press. With her sister Margaret she created and manages the *Crochet Coral Reef* as a worldwide feminist art happening. Works from this project have been widely exhibited including at the 2019 Venice Biennale and 2021 Helsinki Biennial. Her solo work has been included in the recent exhibitions *Plastic Entanglements* and *The Naked Mind*. From 1993 to 2000 she taught in the department of fine art at Goldsmiths College, London, and from 2001 to 2021 in the department of critical studies at the California Institute of the Arts, Los Angeles. She has a PhD in philosophy and literature from Middlesex University, London, and her current research revolves around the relations between logic, bodies, labor, and materiality. She is a member of the California Forum of the IF-EPFCL (International Forums of the Lacanian Field).

Margaret Wertheim,

cocreator of the *Crochet Coral Reef* project, is a science writer and artist whose work focuses on relations between science and the wider cultural landscape. She is animated by a perspective that science is both a field of conceptual enchantment and a socially embedded activity. Wertheim has authored six books, including *Pythagoras' Trousers*, a history of physics and religion that also considers the millennia-long exclusion of women from this field, and *The Pearly Gates of Cyberspace*, a history of Western concepts of space from Dante to the internet. Her writing has appeared in the *New York Times*, *Washington Post*, *The Guardian*, *Cabinet*, *Aeon*, and many others. With her sister Christine, she cofounded the Institute For Figuring, a Los Angeles-based practice devoted to the aesthetic and poetic dimensions of science and mathematics. Through the IFF, the sisters have created exhibits for the Hayward Gallery in London, Science Gallery in Dublin, Art Center College of Design in Pasdena, and elsewhere. Their *Crochet Coral Reef* project—which fuses art, science, craft, community practice, and environmental reflection—has been exhibited internationally, including at the 2019 Venice Biennale, 2021 Helsinki Biennial, Museum of Arts and Design in New York, and the Smithsonian's National Museum of Natural History in Washington. Margaret has worked on all seven continents and stood on the South Pole. Her TED talk about the Reef has been viewed over 1.5 million times and translated into twenty-two languages.

www.christinewertheim.com, www.margaretwertheim.com, www.crochetcoralreef.org, www.theiff.org

Author Biographies

Heather Davis

is a writer, researcher, and teacher whose work draws on feminist and queer theory to examine ecology, materiality, and contemporary art in the context of settler colonialism. An assistant professor of Culture and Media at the New School in New York, Davis is the coeditor of *Art in the Anthropocene: Encounters among Aesthetics, Politics, Environments, and Epistemologies* and editor of the award-winning collection *Desire Change: Contemporary Feminist Art in Canada.* Her current book project, *Plastic Matter*, reexamines materiality in light of plastic's saturation. She is a member of the Synthetic Collective, an interdisciplinary team of scientists, humanities scholars, and artists who investigate and make visible plastic pollution in the Great Lakes.

Amita Deshpande

was born in a village near Pune, India, and raised in the town of Silvassa. Educated as an IT engineer at Cummins College of Engineering, Pune, she also has a master's degree in management from Purdue University. In the United States she worked extensively in sustainable development and corporate social responsibility before moving back to her home country in 2013, where she founded the environmental recycling organization reCharkha: The EcoSocial Tribe in the city of Pune, with a workshop in the nearby village of Khoripada. At reCharkha Deshpande heads the communication, business development, design, and general management of the organization, as well as the management of its affiliated nonprofit arm, the My EcoSocial Planet Foundation. Through her EcoSocial ventures, Amita dreams of forming an EcoSocial tribe of likeminded individuals who understand that for sustainable economic development it is essential to ensure environmental conservation and overall social development.

Donna Haraway

is Distinguished Professor Emerita in the History of Consciousness Department at the University of California Santa Cruz. She earned her PhD in biology at Yale in 1972 and writes and teaches in science and technology studies, feminist theory, and multispecies studies. She has served as thesis adviser for over sixty doctoral students in several disciplinary and interdisciplinary areas. At UCSC she is an active participant in the Science and Justice Research Center and Center for Creative Ecologies. Attending to the intersection of biology with culture and politics, Haraway's work explores the string figures composed by science fact, science fiction, speculative feminism, speculative fabulation, science and technology studies, and multispecies worlding. Her books include *Staying with the Trouble: Making Kin in the Chthulucene* (2016), *When Species Meet* (2008), *The Companion Species Manifesto* (2003), *Modest_Witness@Second_Millennium* (1997, 2nd ed. 2018), *Simians, Cyborgs, and Women* (1991), and *Primate Visions* (1989). Fabrizio Terranova made a feature-length film about her work, titled *Donna Haraway: Story Telling for Earthly Survival* (2016). With Adele Clarke she coedited *Making Kin Not Population* (Prickly Paradigm Press, 2018), which addresses questions of human numbers;

228

feminist, anti-racist, reproductive, and environmental justice; and multispecies flourishing.

Doug Harvey

has been monitoring the Institute For Figuring's *Crochet Coral Reef* from its inception. Since graduating with an MFA in painting from UCLA in 1994, he has juggled multiple careers as a critic, curator, educator, and multimedia artist. He has published over half a million words about the Los Angeles and international art scenes and other aspects of culture for *LA WEEKLY* (where he was lead art critic for
thirteen years), *Art issues*, *Art in America*, *The New York Times*, *The Nation*, *Modern Painters*, and many other publications of note. He has written museum and gallery catalog essays for Jeffrey Vallance, Tim Hawkinson, Marnie Weber, Jim Shaw, Lari Pittman, Georganne Deen, Gary Panter, Margaret Keane, Mike Kelley, Thomas Kinkade, and many others. Two of his curatorial projects caused traffic disruptions on the I-10 freeway. On the occasion of Harvey's mid-career survey at LA Valley College, *LA Times'* Pulitzer-prize winning critic Christopher Knight commented "the raging torrent of modern media-culture is his medium, and the paintings, collages, drawings and sculpture seem to regard it as a revealing cesspool of bleak but salvageable fun." His collection of moldy slides is the subject of a forthcoming monograph published by Strange Attractor. More of his writings, moldy slides, etc. can be found at dougharvey.la, lessart.wordpress.com, and dougharvey.blogspot .com, as well as scattered through the physical world. His faith in science, craft, and feminism dates to his preteen years.

Udo Kittelmann

is a curator and the artistic director of the Museum Frieder Burda. Following a period as artistic director at the Kunstverein Ludwigsburg from 1993 to 1994, he was the director of the Kölnischer Kunstverein in Cologne until 2001. In 2002 he became the director of the Museum für Moderne Kunst (MMK) in Frankfurt am Main, where he remained for six years. From 2008 to 2020 Kittelmann was the director of the Nationalgalerie at the Staatliche Museen zu Berlin, a post that encompasses six museums. Since 2021 he has been in charge of the exhibition program at the Museum Frieder Burda. Kittelmann was commissioner and curator of the German Pavilion at the 49th Venice Biennale and was awarded the Golden Lion for his presentation of Gregor Schneider's *Totes Haus u r*. He curated the Russian Pavilion at the 55th Venice Biennale with the installation *Danaë* by Vadim Zakharov. He has persistently challenged curatorial practice and the institutional treatment of art for many years. His approach is not limited to aesthetic considerations but reflects his awareness of current sociopolitical contexts.

Kayleigh Perkov

is a design historian who studies the intersection of craft and technology. She received her PhD from the Department of Visual Studies at the University of California, Irvine. Her dissertation, "Giving Form to Feedback: Craft and Technology circa 1968–1974," examined the impact of information-age concepts and technology upon craft practice, while arguing that the projects that emerged serve as important precursors to the world of personal technology we know today. She is currently working on a book project that extends this research. Perkov was a recent curatorial fellow with the Center for Craft, a visiting scholar at the Feminist Research Institute at UC Davis, and is a member of the editorial board for *The Journal of Modern Craft*. Her research has been generously supported by the Smithsonian American Art Museum, the Center for Craft, and the Newkirk Center for Science and Society.

Cord Riechelmann

is a Berlin-based journalist and author. He studied biology and philosophy at the Free University in Berlin. Riechelmann was a lecturer on the social behavior of primates and the history of biology research, and he also worked as a columnist and an "urban nature" reporter for the Berlin pages of the *Frankfurter Allgemeine Zeitung*. His research focuses on the living conditions of nature in the culture of urban environments. His books on animals, such as *Bestiarum* (2003) and *Wilde Tiere in der Grossstadt* (2004), straddle philosophy, art, and natural sciences. In 2008 Riechelmann published a CD collection on the voices of animals in Europe, Asia, and Africa. He was cocurator of the special program "Cinema of Animals" at the International Short Film Festival Oberhausen in 2011. *Krähe*, his book on crows, was published in 2013.

Photo Credits

Nikolay Kazakov, Karlsruhe: pp. 9–16, 45, 120–68

The Institute For Figuring, Margaret Wertheim, 2021: pp. 20, 24, 28, 32–33, 43, 45, 48, 52–53, 72–73, 78–79, 82–87, 89–90, 92, 96–98, 100, 168, 189, 194–201, 205, 208–11

The Institute For Figuring, Rebecca Rickman: pp. 1, 17, 65, 70, 130–33, 208–09, 212–17, 232

The Institute For Figuring, Alyssa Gorelick: pp. 38, 49, 62, 203–04, 206–07

The Institute For Figuring, Christina Simons: pp. 80, 198

The Institute For Figuring, Cameron Allen: pp. 88, 93

The Institute For Figuring, Francine McDougall: p. 201

Dr. Axt: pp. 34, 202

Museum Frieder Burda, Baden-Baden: pp. 26–28, 50, 52, 78–79, 110, 115

Cabinet magazine, Brian McMullen: p. 87

Tija Viksna, Galerie Consiento, Riga: p. 33

Eat Pomegranate Photography: p. 94

The M.C. Escher Company— The Netherlands: p. 81

Jeff Elstone: p. 94

Grandma Moses Properties Co / Bridgeman Images: p. 56

Museum Kunst der Westküste, Föhr, 2012: pp. 32–33, 36–37, 43

Nick Greco, Southampton, Pennsylvania: p. 42

Doug Harvey: p. 55

Helsinki Art Museum / Helsinki Biennial, 2021: p. 32

Keith Henderson: p. 87

Museo Larco, Lima: p. 24

Lehigh University Art Galleries, LUAG by Stephanie Veto: pp. 186–87, 190–92

Museum of Arts and Design, New York, MAD by Jenna Bascom: pp. 184–85, 188–89, 192–93

The Metropolitan Museum of Art, New York: pp. 60–61

Guido Mocafico, Paris: pp. 116, 118–19

reCharkha—the EcoSocial Tribe: pp. 102, 104–06

Sammlung Prinzhorn, Universitätsklinikum, Heidelberg: p. 54

Sarah Simons: p. 71

Souls Grown Deep, Atlanta: p. 59

Taxonomy design by Kimberly Varella: pp. 218–19

Francesco Galli, 58th Biennale di Venezia, May You Live in Interesting Times: pp. 66–68

Italo Rondinella, 58th Biennale di Venezia, May You Live in Interesting Times: p. 35

Wikimedia Commons: pp. 22, 74–76, 108, 111

This catalog is published in conjunction with the exhibition

Margaret and Christine Wertheim: Value and Transformation of Corals

Museum Frieder Burda, Baden-Baden
January 29 to June 26, 2022

Edited by Udo Kittelmann for the Frieder Burda Foundation
and by Christine Wertheim and Margaret Wertheim

The exhibition was curated by Udo Kittelmann

Production editor:
Judith Irrgang

Exhibition managers:
Judith Irrgang & Christiane Righetti

Baden-Baden Satellite Reef
administration:
Saskia Kohler

Exhibition design:
mvprojekte, Meyer Voggenreiter
with Nicole Miller

Museum Frieder Burda

Director:
Henning Schaper

Artistic director:
Udo Kittelmann

Head of the collection:
Judith Irrgang

Curatorial assistance:
Christiane Righetti

Administration and marketing:
Annette Smetanig

Office:
Carolin Melcher, Saskia Kohler

Press and public relations:
Kathrin Luz, Ute Rosenfeld

Art education:
Kathrin Dorfner, Brigitte Schoen

Finances:
Jürgen Aßmus

Installation team:
Josef Merkel, Arnd Merkle,
Jannis Müller-Jehle, Ralph Vollmer,
Lukas Stöcker, Karlheinz Zachmann

Catalog

Graphic design:
Margarethe Hausstätter ExtraGestaltung

Translation (Riechelmann essay)
and copyediting:
Tas Skorupa, Berlin

Project management, Wienand:
Johanna Gielen

Production:
Wienand Verlag

Printed in Germany

Published by
Wienand Verlag
www.wienand-verlag.de
Weyertal 59, 50937 Cologne

ISBN 978-3-86832-688-8 (English edition)
ISBN 978-3-86832-676-5 (German edition)

Cover image → *Baden-Baden Satellite Reef*, Museum Frieder Burda, Baden-Baden, 2022, detail
Image, page 1 → *Pod World—Eye Jellies* by Margaret Wertheim and Christine Wertheim, see p. 179
Image, page 232 → Crochet hyperbolic sea creature by Christine Wertheim

The *Baden-Baden Satellite Reef* was made possible by a grant from

Media partner